Up Fanno Creek

Confessions of

an

Accidental Advocate

*TO THE KIDWELLS —
WELCOME TO YOUR NEW
WATERSHED ADDRESS. HOPE
YOU'LL GET AS MUCH OUT
OF IT AS I'VE GOTTEN OUT
OF MINE !*

Eric L____ 3/24/2014

text and photographs by

Eric L. Lindstrom, Ed.D

Portland, Oregon

2012

Ordering Information:

Special discounts are available on quantity purchases by schools, corporations, associations, retailers and others. For details, contact the publisher at the email address above.

Printed by CreateSpace, an Amazon Company

ISBN 978-0-988 1884-0-2

First Edition

To my grandchildren
Chloe, Quinn, Jake and Jane
and
To Watershed Folk Everywhere

Jake crawling for crawdads in Fanno Creek at Bauman Park

ACKNOWLEDGEMENTS

*Writing is easy. All you do is sit staring at a blank piece of paper
until drops of blood form on your forehead.*
—Gene Fowler[1]

On more than one occasion I came close to giving up on this book. The field
work was great fun, but writing up the research was pure hell. I weathered each
of these critical junctures thanks mostly to four sources of inspiration and de-
termination. The first of these was the unflagging support of my family. They
were not only my biggest fans; they were also some of my most valued critics.
I'd especially like to thank my son, Aaron, and my wife, Kitty, for reading early
drafts and offering detailed editorial advice.

In addition to my family, more than 150 people—virtually all of them total
strangers to begin with—granted me access, time, and information as I struggled to comprehend the workings of the watershed. Whenever my enthusiasm
for the project would begin to fade, I would remind myself of the great debt I
owed these generous, patient and trusting souls. I'd also remind myself that
the only way I could repay that debt was by finishing the project they had tac-
itly agreed to support when they let me into their professional—and sometimes
personal—lives. This is their book, as much as it is mine.

A third wellspring of inspiration and drive came from a few key Watershed
Folk who ended up mentoring me through most of the last five years: Kendra
Smith took me under her wing and guided me through the complex organization
of the watershed management business; Sue Manning helped me reconnect to
all that is great and good in education, whether it happens in a classroom or on
the banks of a stream; and Brian Wegner pushed me in front of every watershed
issue he could find, and taught me how to think like an advocate even before I
knew I had become one.

Finally, whenever all else seemed to have failed, there was always Fanno
Creek, just a few blocks away, beckoning for another visit. It took a while before I fully realized how much the two of us needed each other; but when I
finally made that connection, there was no turning back.

---

1   As quoted by TerriblyWrite.com (2012)

TABLE OF CONTENTS

Book I—A Thousand Cuts

Book II—A Million Trees

Book One:

A Thousand Cuts

Wetlands buried alive in the first stages of development of a commercial property in Tigard

Ki-a-kuts bridge as seen from inside the mouth of Fanno Creek

1—Into the Urban Bush

Rivulets

Up ahead one of the road crew flipped her traffic sign to "Stop" and the cars in front of me ground to a halt. A front-loader began jockeying a large sheet of steel into position over a gaping hole in the road. Suddenly, a chain parted. A corner of the plate dug into the concrete. The stress broke another chain, and the plate bucked, jerked and whipped around, out of control. A workman guiding the plate with a shovel jumped back. His fast reflexes had left him unscathed, but he was cursing loudly for all of that. We were going to be stuck here awhile.

I turned off the truck, rolled down the windows and let in the warm June breeze. The scent of cottonwoods filled the car. The fragrance revived memories of fishing and exploration along the banks of a creek that ran through the back-forty of Old Man Bronson's pig farm. Me and Bobby Buchanan, two scrawny 12-year-old boys, stomping along in clear, shallow, fast-running water; hands full of minnow buckets and short-handled nets; pockets stuffed full of treasures retrieved from the creek bed—mostly broken, water-tumbled crystals that were pretty when wet but dull and drab when dry—shirt fronts bulging with crumpled bags of potato chips and peanut butter sandwiches wrapped in waxed paper. A dozen or two blue-pincered crawdads scratched along the bottoms of one of the buckets. Eight terrified minnows dashed back and forth above them in the sloshing water. A ninth floated upside down, gills flared out and belly beginning to bloat. It was the summer of 1955.

The clang of metal on metal pulled me out of my reverie. Several workers were standing around with their hands on their hips, while another was using a sledge hammer to do something wonderfully loud to the iron plate. The road work had brought my truck to a halt in the center of the small bridge that spans Fanno Creek, just south of the intersection of Allen Street and Scholls Ferry Road. I had been up and down this street hundreds of times since moving to Portland's West Slope neighborhood in 1999, but this was the first time I'd ever really noticed the creek. I got out of the truck, ambled over to the railing and peered into the darkness of the creek bed. It wasn't much to look at, just a gravel-bottomed stream with a trickle of clear water running over it. The flow was subdued, lethargic even. Only the filaments of string algae waving slowly in the current betrayed the languid westerly direction of its movement. A rotting tennis shoe lay halfway out of the water on the left bank. The top of a half-submerged beer can winked at me from the shallows on the right. Trees and low brush crowded the tops of both banks, a green buffer between the creek and the surrounding houses and apartments. The banks on either side were steep and heavily eroded. The stream vanished from sight behind a thicket of bushes just west of the bridge. Something about the look of the place suggested that from time to time large volumes of fast-moving water passed through here.

After a few minutes reflection I decided it wasn't all that different from the creek Bobby and I splashed through as we built our baitfish empire. I shook my head, thinking of the physical impact we must have made as we moved up and down the stream each day. We literally left no stone unturned and no pool un-seined. A dozen minnows netted us a quarter; as many crawdads would pull down twice that much. Fortunately for the environment, we never focused on business for very long. There were too many wonderful distractions in the stream and along the bank.

The sound of engines starting sent me scurrying back to the truck. The flagger quickly ditched her cigarette, then flipped the sign from red to yellow. Whatever happened to Bobby, I wondered? My God, it's been half a century almost. Would I recognize him if I passed him on the street today? Was he still living in Arkansas? I'd heard that when he was in high school he had lost his dad. Did he make it out of the 1960s, or did he end up dead somewhere in Vietnam, like so many others from that era? I forced my mind to abandon such profitless introspection and put it to work on the nearest, most neutral subject at hand: What about this scrawny little creek? Where did the water come from and where was it headed? I had a map in the glove compartment and there was a gas station coming up on my right. I pulled in, fueled up, and minutes later was headed for the top of the Fanno Creek watershed.

Headwaters

Just a few blocks to the west of downtown Portland a high ridge separates the city from its far-southwestern neighborhoods. It also separates most of Multnomah County from Washington County and the Tualatin River Basin. Depending upon the conversational context, it's known as the Tualatin Mountains, Tualatin Hills or the West Hills.[1] Several of its peaks are over a thousand feet high; most of these have two or more red and white radio towers perched on their shaved heads. One such antenna farm sits atop TV Hill, a barren, 22-acre dome. At 1,070 feet, this is the highest promontory in the Fanno Creek sub-basin. A narrow road—SW 57th Street—runs along the western crest of the hilltop. I parked on the narrow shoulder of the road bordering the antenna farm's security fence, then got out of the truck and began looking around for some sign of a waterway.

---

1 I will usually refer to this area as the Tualatin Hills. This is the Pacific Northwest, and for most folks up here a pile of rock isn't properly a mountain until it reaches an elevation of 1,500 feet, the average height of the Coast Range.

A weed-choked ditch along the uphill side of the roadway led to a culvert that exited on the downhill side of the roadway's steep embankment. The end of this iron pipe stuck out over a small ravine that trailed away to the west. The ditch and the pipe were bone dry. So was the splash pan several feet below it. I scraped away some gravel with a stick and poked at the dirt below with my fingers. Hardpan and dry as a bone. Down slope from the splash area the stream channel vanished into a clump of shrubs.

Everything about the place suggested that this was the top of Fanno Creek— everything except the fact that there wasn't a drop of water. I got back in the truck and revisited the map, this time with the magnifying glass I habitually carry these days. The blue line on the map led west from where I sat for a half mile, then turned sharply to the south for a couple of miles more before splitting into two segments. One headed south towards the Tualatin River; the other went east in the general direction of Hillsdale. I was already at the top of what I'd thought was the most likely headwaters candidate, but it had proven to be a dry hole, in the most literal sense. The only other candidate appeared to be located in Hillsdale.

As I drove off the hill, I reflected for the first time on the nature of urban watersheds. How might they vary from their country cousins? Who "owns" them? How are they managed? Surely they are managed. Where does the water come from when there's been no rain for days and days? There's no snow pack within fifty miles. How common were springs in these parts? How could I have lived here for almost ten years and know nothing about this creek?

My street map indicated that the stream in the Hillsdale neighborhood rose in a small triangular area squeezed in among several well-established neighborhoods. A couple of city streets, one of them a very busy thoroughfare, connected just above the spot where water presumably first appeared in the streambed. Could there really be a spring in that area?

Another logical source for water was human activity. This line of thought quickly led me to questions about the overall management of urban streams. Who was responsible for the health and well-being of these urban drainages? Was it possible that municipalities released treated sewer waters into these small neighborhood streams, just as they released them into rivers, lakes and oceans?

A particularly beautiful fall morning back in the mid-1980s suddenly came to mind. I was fishing for salmon in Agate Pass, the strait between Bainbridge Island and the Kitsap Peninsula in Washington. As the boat drifted along in the relatively smooth waters surrounding the rip current, I noticed what appeared to be shreds of toilet paper tumbling around in the surge. Yes, my guide informed me, it was indeed toilet paper. But not to worry—the salmon wouldn't be eating it. Many of the residences on both banks still pumped raw sewage into Puget Sound then—legally or not. Was it possible, I wondered now, that some of the water in the Fanno Creek system came from local toilets/sewer systems, too? I couldn't imagine that being the case, not in this day and age.

I parked on Old Bertha Road, a side street just off Beaverton-Hillsdale Highway, and walked north across a vacant lot and into a dense thicket of young trees. They marked the head of what turned out to be a fairly deep ravine. Somewhere, way down in what looked like an impenetrable jungle of ivy and blackberries, was the top of Fanno Creek—or so suggested the map. In between the noise of passing cars and buses I thought I could hear the faint but distinct sound of trickling water. I wasn't dressed for rough work that day—street jeans, a light-weight cotton shirt, a pair of tennis shoes—but I decided to enter the underbrush anyway.

I felt a little weird about striking off into the Urban Bush like that. For one thing, I wasn't sure it was legal. There were no warning signs or fence that I could see, but it didn't make sense that this kind of at-will ingress was acceptable. How could it be that an area like this was completely uncontrolled? What manner of stuff might I find down there? The thought of stumbling upon a dead body or something equally ghastly made me pause a moment before going on. I had no idea what to expect, and for the first time (but not the last) I asked myself what the hell I was up to.

A few feet from the brush-crowded sidewalk the embankment dropped off at an alarmingly steep rate. The upper portions of the embankment were overgrown with blackberry bushes. They tore at my street clothes and my exposed skin. Later I would learn how to move safely through this kind of vicious underbrush, but this first time out I was shredded before I had descended a dozen feet.

A little deeper into the ravine the sounds of the highway traffic fell away abruptly, and the odd, semi-silence added considerably to the strangeness of the situation. In what I decided later was an optical illusion, the tree canopy seemed to close in above me as I continued downward. The ground beneath the underbrush was loose and moved continually beneath my feet. Would my footing hold, or would it give way, sending me and the small bushes I clung to tumbling into the bottom of the ravine? The briars and the ivy were getting so dense that I couldn't actually see where I was putting my feet. As a kid I was prone to stepping on nails. The thought of a sudden puncture wound made me shuffle along rather than lift my feet. When had I last had a tetanus shot?

Shuffling along made navigating through the brambles much harder, and several times I tripped and nearly went down. I tried to see ahead, but for the most part I had to make my way on faith through the thick brush, trusting that my next step would be secure and painless. Blackberries and other light-loving vegetation had given way to a nearly impenetrable mat of ivy that flowed around the trees, crawling high on their spindly trunks. Just a few feet further down the mat flattened out for a bit, then headed up the other side of the ravine. I was very near the bottom and, judging by the sound, the creek should have been directly underfoot.

Suddenly the ground went out from under me. As I pitched forward onto the ivy I braced myself for a hard landing that never came. Instead, I was stretched out full length, bouncing gently as if on a trampoline. I was lying on the flattened remains of a wire fence, which at one time must have protected the channel from interlopers. I pulled back the ivy covering the section of fence directly in front of me and looked down at the headwaters of Fanno Creek.

Protruding from an embankment was the first foot or two of a rusted pipe maybe two feet in diameter. A steady trickle of clear water fell from its lip and splattered into a splash pool three feet below. The streambed trailed away from the pool, its bottom filled with rocks of varying diameter, all of them covered in a brown, furry coat of algae below the water line. I lay there, staring at the brown and green rocks in the splash pool, and considered my next move. First I would need to get back to the street, no mean feat. Just getting off the fence was going take some doing. Somehow, I regained a vertical orientation and began clawing my way up the slope. The embankment that had been soft and crumbly in spots on the way down now simply disintegrated under each step. I lost footing and fell several times, once face first into a particularly nasty patch of blackberries. I wrapped my bandana around my right hand, improvising a glove that allowed me to grab some of the more stationary blackberries and pull myself out of the abyss. It was getting very warm in the ravine, and by now the numerous scratches on my body were stinging from sweat. Grunting and cursing, I finally emerged from the bush, stepped out onto the sidewalk and practically knocked over a woman who was waiting for a bus. "Lost a hubcap," I mumbled.

Back in the truck, I dabbed at my bleeding scratches with the bandana while I studied the map once more. The confluence of the creek and the Tualatin River was just fifteen minutes away. Just north of where they met, the creek ran through Durham City Park. Its wiggly shape on the map reminded me of a diagram of the lower intestines. My map gave no indication of how to get into Durham's park, but just across the river from the confluence was another park and its access points were clearly marked. The afternoon was winding down but there was plenty of daylight left. I absentmindedly wiped a few drops of sweat and blood off the map, then started the truck and headed south.

Confluence

One of the best ways to get a sense of the relationship between Fanno Creek and the Tualatin River is to approach their confluence from the south side of the river. This approach involves a short walk north through the city of Tualatin's Community Park, and it puts you directly across from the place where Fanno Creek finally completes its 14-mile odyssey, delivering itself to the river. Signage memorializing the flood-ridden history of the town conveys a solid sense of how dynamic river systems can be. The most recent heavy flooding along this stretch of the river took place in 1996. Rapid melting of snow pack and heavy rain in the Coast Range, combined with a succession of heavy downpours in eastern Washington County, forced both the river and Fanno Creek over their banks and into much of the immediate countryside. At various places in the park (and elsewhere along the river), markers have been erected to show the height of the floodwaters during that historic deluge. The soft surface trail leading through the eastern portion of the park follows the main channel of the river. In most places the river itself is downslope a good 30 feet or more. As I walked along the path and looked down the steep bank at the river more than 20 feet below, it was hard to believe that in April of 1996 the top of my head would have been completely submerged.

The north end of the trail connects to a concrete path leading onto a relatively new pedestrian bridge.[2] I walked out to the center of the span, leaned on the rail and surveyed the river below. The first time I took a canoe ride on this river, my guide told me that if we tipped over I shouldn't try to swim. Just stand up. Someone in the next canoe said, "No, no, don't do that. You'll disappear in the mud!" They were joking, but not much. During all but the wettest months of the year the river is a wide, shallow, muddy flow. In some places there is so little current that it doesn't appear to move at all. The bottom in all but its uppermost reaches is a deep bed of extremely fine silt dragged down from the surrounding mountains or sloughed off by the thousands of acres of farmland that still crowd much of the river's main channel. Snow and rain drive the Tualatin and, except for the wettest periods, there's never a lot of water in it. The river's headwaters are located high in the Coast Range to the west. These areas were heavily forested once, but now it's hard to find a hilltop that hasn't been shaved down to its huckleberries at least a couple times.

The river drops 1,800 feet in the first dozen miles of its run, then takes another 60 miles to drop an additional 250 feet. The stretch between River Mile 33 and River Mile 3.4, one of the river's longest sections, is also one of its flattest, dropping less than 2 feet in roughly 30 miles. More than 50 miles of the riv-

---

2   In 2010 the bridge was dedicated to Ki-A-kuts, an Atfalati Indian who served as spokesperson for his people during some of the negotiations that led to their removal to the Grande Ronde reservation in 1857. More about the Atfalati in the Chapter titled *Children of the Flood*.

er's main stem run through one of the most fertile valleys in the United States. Much of this valley was put hard to the plow for more than 150 years; these days more and more of it is vanishing under an ever-growing wave of residential and commercial development. For the most part, this urbanization is moving east to west across the floor of the Tualatin Basin, spreading out from the Portland hub like ripples on a pond.

Fanno Creek somewhat resembles the Tualatin River. It starts high, drops fast and finishes long and low. It crawls through its streambed when the weather is dry but charges down it like a freight train whenever a good-sized rain storm comes along. Hydrologists, the folks who study stream behaviors, describe this kind of flow as "flashy." This flashiness is one of the main reasons why every year Fanno Creek ends up carrying prodigious amounts of silt out of the Tualatin Hills and into the river.

In the geophysical scheme of things the confluence of a creek with its river is a dynamic relationship. The two streams are perpetually reorienting themselves to the terrain and to each other. As a result, their confluence is more a zone than a discrete point. This zone shifts continually from one area to another, sometimes dramatically so. When Oregon was young, and only Indian trails crisscrossed the landscape of Washington County, Fanno Creek and the Tualatin River had nearly a thousand acres of mud and well-vegetated wetlands within which they could periodically renegotiate the location of their confluence.

About a hundred years ago, a railroad bridge linking the town of Tualatin to points north was built over the river and its floodplain. In the following decades the roadbed was repeatedly beefed up, so much so that it now acts as a levy, effectively trapping most of the creek's immediate floodplain against a steep bluff that lies directly east of the tracks. The floodplain at the confluence is now less than 300 acres. It runs almost due north-south, parallel to the rail line, and in some places the distance between the tracks and the bluff on the east side is less than 300 feet.

I crossed to the river's north shore on a bridge erected in 2007, one which further complicated the creek's life. It stands just a hundred feet or so inside the scanty floodplain still remaining between the railroad and the bluff. The landforms on the south side of the river are higher here than those on the north bank, meaning that a second levy-like approach had to be built for the roadway that leads bike and foot traffic back and forth between the two parks. This has significantly reduced to just over 300 feet the space in which the river and the creek may interact during years of normal rainfall.

These days the mouth of Fanno Creek is shoved up so tightly against the bridge's abutment that it's sometimes hard to see it from the southern shore.

That was especially the case on my first visit to the confluence. I'd hit the area in the height of the growing season. A dense curtain of vegetation hung so far out over the river that it completely obscured the banks below.

The view from the north end of the bridge was completely different. Here, I could look down on the confluence twenty feet below. A small nub of land stuck out from the intersection of the creek's right bank and the river's left,[3] an obvious fishing spot judging from its orientation towards the creek and the well-worn path leading to it from the end of the bridge. It was a steep path; navigating it in wetter times would have been a difficult task. Several well-placed bushes provided handholds, and in no time I was standing on the nub, right next to an iron pipe that had been driven into the ground as a pole holder.

I watched for a while as the creek pumped itself out of its bed and into the river. It had been awhile since the last rain, so the creek was relatively free of sediment. As a result, the flow created a brief clearing in the otherwise muddy body of the larger stream.[4] A few tiny whirlpools kept forming and disbursing in an arc along the downstream side of the confluence. Some ducks quacked along the upstream shoreline and I heard a red-tailed hawk calling in the distance. People, many on bikes, came and went across the bridge. Occasionally a hapless insect floated by, usually on its back, legs going like mad as it tried to right itself and escape the glue-like grip of the water molecules. At one point a long, narrow stream of bright green, freshly cut grass clippings undulated past my perch.

Without thinking much about it I held a stick out to a drowning honey bee. She managed to grab hold long enough for me to put her somewhere that she could dry off in relative safety. I didn't hear any kids. Would I have let my kids play in this creek, I wondered? Probably not. A bulky bed roll tucked up in the bridge's substructure, the remnants of a recently used campfire and a well-worn bald spot on the ground just below the abutment suggested frequent use by transients.

Another insect, a black beetle floating on its back, legs waving madly in the air, struggled by just out of my reach. The current caught the hapless critter and bore it slowly towards the east. It dawned on me that the insect was only a few confluences away from the Pacific Ocean. I wondered if he, or at least his pitiful little carcass, might make the full run. Somehow it didn't seem too great a distance. From the bridge the river flows on for another ten miles east to the town of West Linn, where its waters mingle with those of the Willamette River. From West Linn the Willamette's waters head thirty miles north until

3 You orient yourself to a stream by looking downstream. In that position the bank on your right is the right bank.
4 Extreme rain events, improperly managed land use activities or occasional landslides in the Fanno Creek watershed can result in the creek carrying loads of sediment relatively higher than those of the river even in the winter time.

they rendezvous with the mighty Columbia River, which in turn pushes into the Pacific Ocean another hundred miles to the north and west. The beetle's journey would be less than 150 miles. What manner of other little gifts might Fanno Creek carry to the sea on a regular basis in its flotsam and jetsam? What were the relative volumes of water involved, Fanno Creek to the Tualatin, to the Willamette, to the Columbia? The questions kept coming.

From looking at my map I already knew that Fanno Creek ran through parts of three counties and five cities. What kinds of conversations concerning Fanno Creek took place among these various governments and how often? How did Metro—the Portland area's regional government—interact with the creek? Which agencies, state and federal, had a role in the creek's affairs? What did communications among the big watershed guns and local jurisdictions look like? And who were "the big watershed guns" anyway?

A sharp "snick" came from the surface just a few feet away from the bank. The dark shape of a fish below the swirl vanished as it sped towards deeper water. The twice-unlucky beetle would not be making it to the Pacific, after all. My mother came to mind, perhaps because she would have seen the beetle's fate coming long before the final moment. "When I fish," she once told me, "I don't *think* about anything, I just visualize the fish. When I get a nibble I can see the fish bumping the bait with my mind's eye; and I almost always know when I'm going to get a strike because I can see him, just as if I were watching it all from underwater. I can even see the bait move when I mooch it with my pole."

A dog's bark from somewhere along the path above brought my mind back to the moment. I'd been hunkered down next to the creek so long that my legs were numb. I stood up and headed back up to bridge level. I'd been fishing, I realized, as surely as if there'd been a pole in my hands. Not for some hapless fish, but for something else. The dim shape of a concept was floating around in the murkiness of my brain. I continued to mooch for it as I reached the deck of the bridge and headed back towards the truck. At mid-span I stopped and looked back at the confluence. The sun had dropped low enough to put the area in deep shadow. No one walking the bridge at that hour would have noticed the creek unless they already knew where it was. If it hadn't been for the frame of reference provided by the bridge abutment, I might not have been able to fully differentiate the inlet from the rest of the river bank, myself.

When I reached the truck I just sat there for a while, drinking cold coffee directly out of the thermos and watching the last highlights disappear from the nearby playground equipment. Suddenly I was very tired. I started the truck and headed home.

Tributaries

For a long time I'd known, at least in a general sort of way, what I would do if and when I had the opportunity to retire: I would indulge in an orgy of learning. For most of my life the only thing more active than my imagination had been my curiosity. I was going to let them both run ahead of me as far as practical circumstances allowed. Maybe even further. Exactly how I was going to manage the process I wasn't completely sure; but I thought I might try to return to my photo-journalistic roots and retool a new career in photography and writing.

I had started down that pathway once before, right after I left the Marines. I'd gone to college with every intention of becoming a shooter for *National Geographic*, and that kind of photography continued to be my main interest until a couple of days before graduation when my first daughter was born. I was at my wife's side during the delivery, still the exception at that time. It was an experience that's been equaled twice more, but never rivaled. It's no exaggeration to say that after one look at that kid I was no longer interested in being on the road 11 months out of the year. I immediately went about the task of switching to a less risky, potentially more profitable, career in advertising photography.

It turned out to be a good decision. I built up a solid client base and began making a decent living. Still, while the business provided a semblance of financial stability, I felt a gap where a sense of creative development was concerned. I decided to try to fill it with some part-time teaching at the community college level.

The teaching turned out to be addictive, and for a while I found ways to juggle a career in the field and a second one in the classroom. Then, in the early 1990s, I had the chance to manage some evening degree and diploma programs designed for adult learners. The deal also included an opportunity to go back to school and earn a master's degree in adult education. The down sides were considerable: not only would I have to leave the field of photography, I'd have to leave the instructional ranks as well. In the end, having a shot at an advanced degree was more temptation than I could resist.

I loved grad school with a passion. I was much older than any of the other students and even a couple of the professors, and for a while that worried me. But by the end of the first semester I knew I was in exactly the right spot at exactly the right time. Being able to study adult learning theory one evening, then turn around and apply theory to practice the next made the experience the most satisfying of my entire academic career.

About the same time I began working on my master's degree I started making occasional excursions into the eastern portions of Washington. I was particularly fascinated by the in-your-face character of the area's geology. The less well-developed spaces of the state's eastern half ultimately became a kind of informal lab in which I began spending as much time as possible studying natural history. We lived in the Seattle area at the time, and because of work restraints I was generally required to limit the length of my outings to a few days. Then, on one particularly far-ranging trip into the extreme southeastern area of Oregon, I visited Steens Mountain for the first time. I fell in love with Oregon as a whole on that trip. I also developed particularly strong feelings for its Dry Side.

The last morning of my stay in the Steens I sat on a rocky outcrop 9,700 feet above sea level and watched the sun spill its light along the rim of the Owyhee Mountains in Idaho, 100 miles to the east. Seconds later a golden flood filled the floor of the Alvord Desert, 5,500 feet directly below my perch. I had a camera in hand, but as I began to raise it to my eye the whole idea of "capturing" such an instant seemed both ludicrous and profane. I opted to simply sit there in dumb amazement while the light burned an indelible memory into my brain.

When an opportunity came to leave Seattle and move to Portland I jumped at it. The new assignment not only involved a substantial promotion, it also included the opportunity to work for another advanced degree, this time a doctorate in education. The decade that followed was one of the most eventful and rewarding periods of my life. At the same time it was also one of the most difficult and wearing. Year after year the bright spots in education that had sustained my progress for almost two decades slowly faded away, until all that seemed to be illuminated were legal-sized sheets of computer generated data. Then one day the last light went out; even the data ceased to be of any genuine interest to me. It was time to move on.

Leaving the workplace and entering retirement was like stepping from a car after a long ride out of the city and into the desert. The vista was incomparable, open, vast and mysterious; the air was somehow crisper and cleaner, every breath a banquet; and the silence was so profound that all I could hear was the rapid beating of my heart. It was a thrilling experience, but I hadn't been able to stop and savor it for long before Fanno Creek came meandering by.

Ripa Incognita

There's this thing I do I call "grinding." It happens when some issue is in the air and won't come down. It can be a big issue or a little one; it doesn't seem to matter. So long as it remains unsettled I can't leave it alone. It's kind of like getting a particular tune stuck in your head, usually one you can't stand, and being unable to make it go away. A few days after my visit to the confluence I woke up at 3:00 a.m., grinding away on the creek and what to do about it. I knew that getting back to sleep was out of the question, so I got out of bed, went downstairs to my office and began surfing the net. I started by plugging in variations on the word "watershed." I hate to read off the monitor, so I simply plugged in a few strings, printing and skimming as I went. When the printer spat out the last list of 30 hits, I leaned back and began going through the printouts with an old-fashioned highlighter. Anything that seemed potentially interesting got a big, orange swipe across it. Suddenly I came to the phrase "watershed address" and even as the marker zipped across the words a light went on in my brain.

There are magical moments in the learning process. "Ah-hah!" moments they're called, and I had one right then and there. The concept of having a personal address based upon the physical structure of the land—a particular place in time and space—captured my imagination. I began mining the web, and by the time the sun began streaming into the windows behind my desk, I had decided to explore the creek from top to bottom. To make the project even more interesting I would write a book about the process. The decision brought with it a deep sense of peace. I went upstairs, kissed my wife on the cheek as she headed off to work and climbed back into bed.

A few days later I set up the journal I've kept ever since the project formally began. On its cover is the date (6/26/2007) and the following diagram:

-> GO...LOOK...SEE...REFLECT...UNDERSTAND -> GO...
know the watershed

Over the last five years this diagram has served multiple purposes. Sometimes it's been a battle cry, an exhortation to get re-steamed about the work involved. At other times it's been a motto or statement of purpose. Above all, it's served as a kind of curriculum map. In brief, a curriculum map is a tool educators use to help themselves identify and understand the interrelationships of all the components of an educational program. There are actually four steps to the mapping process: planning, implementation, assessment, and re-planning.

From the outset I wanted my study to develop through a special kind of intimacy with the creek, a relationship that would be built from the streambed up. When I used the word "know" I was focusing less on its objective meaning and more on its existential overtones. I wanted to be able to look out of the creek as well as into it. In this context the diagram contained an implicit set of instructions or guidelines and filled out to something like this:

GO—Travel through the entirety of the watershed and stand quietly in as much of it as possible. Walk along its ridgelines, over its bridges and through its forgotten thickets. Stand in its parking lots and playgrounds and poke around in its residential developments. Above all else stand for long hours in and around the creek. Let the water seep in and fill your shoes.

LOOK—Be transparent and open and let the experiences flow over and through your consciousness in as raw a form as possible. Forget the known or the assumed. Try to enter the watershed unencumbered by a made-up-mind. Be a child, albeit a careful one.

SEE—Make no judgments, rush to no conclusions. Examine your ignorance and let the questioning draw out ever more penetrating questions. Worry about answers only when you are certain you are ready to turn those answers into yet another round of questioning.

REFLECT—Make sense of what you've learned, but not too much sense and never in too much of a hurry. Let the information tumble around with other information until an insight announces itself.

UNDERSTAND—Recognize that understanding is dynamic and that your insights, when and if they come, are never absolute. Be comfortable with the idea that the chief characteristic of understanding is the way it invariably reveals the true dimensions of your ignorance.

GO—Acknowledge the iterative nature of *being* by returning to the watershed over and over again. Celebrate your ignorance by wearing it fearlessly like some sort of badge. Hope to be even more surprised and puzzled the next time around. And above all, stand quietly for a while in a new place in the stream. Let the water seep in and fill your shoes.

I followed up the development of my curriculum guide with the development of some supporting lesson materials. Chief among these were the beginnings of a fairly extensive collection of maps related to the watershed. A good many of them I pulled off the internet. One of these gave me my first clear sense of one of the watershed's core issues: the fragmented nature of its overall governance. The map was posted on Portland's Bureau of Environmental Services (BES) website.[5]

The bulk of Portland's portion of the Fanno Creek watershed lies within a triangle formed by the intersections of three major highways: State Route 217 to the west, the Sunset Highway to the north and Interstate Highway 5 to the east. In BES's depiction the watershed spreads naturally into the right hand portion of the map. However, the left hand sections are empty. The watershed appears to end abruptly along the north-south boundary denoting the end of Portland's city limits. The remaining 66 percent of Fanno Creek and its tributaries simply ceases to exist. It was visually dissatisfying, but the map was just telling it like it is, jurisdictionally.

The map may have helped me develop some insights into Portland's watershed management priorities, but it was next to useless for planning my research activities. For that I needed something that covered the entire area of the watershed. I searched the internet for a while, but finding nothing that really served, I decided to make my own map.

---

5   Since this portion of the narrative was first written BES has developed a new map of the watershed, one that includes its entirety. While the new map is a substantial improvement over the older version, the multi-jurisdictional issues discussed here and elsewhere in the book remain one of Fanno Creek's major challenges.

To get started I mounted the heart of my road map on a 36 x 28 piece of foam-core board. Then I re-traced every segment of the Fanno Creek system with a thin, dark blue marker. This helped me grasp the shape and scale of the water-shed. It also helped me identify the creek's main tributaries. I counted 20 of these at the time, only a few of which were actually identified on the map. Next I began sticking different colored map pins into places I thought might be accessible as well as interesting. A red one went into the map wherever any of the blue lines designating a tributary began. A white one went in at places where key roadways intersected Fanno Creek or one of its major tributaries. Yellow pins went in at important confluences, and green ones designated any place I had actually managed to visit. That night I was able to stick four green pins into the board—one at the antenna park on Sylvan Hill; one at the "headwaters" off of Old Bertha Road; one at the creek's confluence with the Tualatin; and the last one at the bridge, where my quest had begun just a few days before.

The web of blue lines and the small forest of white pins helped underscore the enormity of the task involved. There were already more than a hundred pins in the map, places that I would need to visit before I could hope to say that I had fully entered the watershed. I pulled an old pair of calipers out of my desk and began making crude measurements. The map's depiction of the main stem of Fanno Creek worked out to be very close to 14 miles. That conformed to information I'd already picked up from a couple of trips to the internet. After a little more work with the calipers I was pretty sure that the entire Fanno System, including all the unnamed segments, incorporated more than 70 miles of stream bank: 14 miles of main stem and more than 20 miles of tributaries, times two. The calculation was crude, to be sure, but it was enough to give me a sense of how much time and effort it might take merely to investigate the entire run of the creek. I was looking at several years of study, not to mention writing it all up. What in the world was I getting myself into?

Partly for fun, but also as a sort of cautionary note to myself I wrote the words *Ripa Incognita* across the top with a black felt-tipped pen—"Unknown Stream." Suspect as the Latin might be, it partly captured the essence of the journey I was about to embark upon.

Local Knowledge

Not all I wanted to learn about the watershed resided in its physical components. There was an entire landscape of information in the form of books, papers and other varieties of documentation that I would need to explore. Thanks to my experiences as a grad student I was comfortable with that part of the task. I had a fairly good idea of how to put together a research project, particularly a case study such as the one I was embarking upon. There was also the matter of obtaining more informal materials, specifically what anthropologists refer to as "local knowledge,"[6] i.e., the lived experiences that take place in a particular environment.

Now I was venturing into entirely new territory—new to me at least. There would be a new vocabulary to master, as well as a whole set of cultural perspectives and behaviors to recognize and understand. And it wouldn't be just one set of cultural perspectives. I already understood that my field work would be taking place in environments ranging from council chambers to sewer pipes. I would be a total outsider.

My first excursions into the urban bush had already taught me two things. First, I needed to gear up, particularly in terms of outerwear. Thanks to the sea of blackberries I encountered on my brief exploration of the headwaters of Fanno Creek, the blue jeans I'd worn had more holes in them than a piece of ostrich skin. I knew I could anticipate getting wet from time to time, but nothing currently in my closet could handle both the blackberries and the heavy winter rains. I had some excellent dry-weather footwear, but again, nothing that would serve once the rains commenced.

Second, I would need some guidance from a few understanding and tolerant souls who might be willing to act as facilitators and guides as I pursued my low adventures along Fanno Creek. In an academic context[7] the human resources components of a study are variously known as "subjects," "actors," "respondents" and "informants." These terms say more about what the researcher is up to than what the person's role in a study may be. In general "subjects" get tested, "actors" are observed and "respondents" answer questions. "Informants" do all those things but go one step further by doing them as part of a process that helps define, and sometimes redefine, the actual research. Except for the fact that informants neither initiate nor conduct the study, they might also be referred to as "collaborators."

As I began sifting through information about various watershed organizations in the area, I started collecting the names and contact information of potential study participants, particularly any who might be potential guides. How do you identify potential candidates when your knowledge base and network of contacts are in their infancies? One way is to keep track of how often someone's name, or even their job title, appears in reference materials. Frequency usually indicates both relevance and a certain level of availability. Another route is to look for the names of people who serve in an informational capacity—e.g., outreach personnel, information officers and the like for public agencies and corporate entities. A great deal of my work would focus on public

6 Raphels, H. (2003)
7 Spradley, J. P. (1979)

Fanno Creek headwaters (top) and Tualatin River confluence (bottom)

and other not-for-profit organizations. Developing contact information where these were concerned would be relatively easy.

Besides being able to find reliable guides, any good explorer needs to develop a good sense for the territory. Fortunately, more often than not a major portion of any exploration is conducted over known, and perhaps even well-traveled, terrain. Consider Alexander von Humboldt,[8] arguably one of the greatest European explorers of all time, and his treks across the southern hemisphere. Many of Humboldt's travel routes into and through the interior of South America were well known to other Europeans, whose explorations of the continent had been going on for 250 years. Quite often he sojourned at waypoints that had been inhabited by Indians for centuries or even millennia before any white man set sail for the New World.

Closer to home, Lewis and Clark benefited from similar good fortune. For most of their journey the Corps of Discovery followed footpaths or trails made by Indians over thousands of years. Many of these had been used by white trappers and mountain men for decades before the Corps set out from St. Louis.

None of this is meant to minimize the incredible accomplishments of these great explorers or others like them. It simply illustrates an important point which is sometimes overlooked: exploration is mostly a collaborative affair. Neither Humboldt nor the Corps would have made it far without tapping the knowledge and other resources of people who had already scouted many of these supposedly unknown lands. Even in the deepest wilderness there are few truly solo human acts.

Exploring Fanno Creek would not involve going into anything like a real wilderness, of course. I wouldn't be gone for years at a time. My cell phone would always be handy if I actually got in trouble. I wasn't likely to run the great personal risks associated with the expeditions mounted by Humboldt or Lewis and Clark. Nor was I likely to suffer, I sincerely hoped, the kind of physical miseries and tests of endurance that both ventures ultimately demanded. Yet my resources would be significantly stretched, particularly my intellectual ones. I would need a great deal of technical assistance and general support from what I anticipated would be a tightly knit community of watershed specialists, scientists, government officials, environmentalists and the like. I already had a name in my mind for this "indigenous" community: Watershed Folk. I could hardly wait to begin meeting them, but first I needed to come to grips with a more fundamental aspect of the watershed—its geology.

8   Helfrich, G. (2003)

The Columbia River Gorge just above The Dalles

2—The Basin's Bones

Bad Day at Imnaha

One day around 16.5 million years ago, somewhere near the present location of the tiny town of Imnaha in northeastern Oregon, all hell broke loose. For critters in the immediate area the event began badly, and as the day wore on it didn't get any better. The ground heaved and pitched as thousands of earthquakes, some of unbelievable magnitude, announced the End of Days for all living things that couldn't run or fly fast enough to get out of the way. Countless faults spread across the land on such a large scale that it must have seemed the entire world was coming apart at its seams. To a certain extent, that was exactly what was about to happen. Great rips would open up across the landscape, some of them thousands of feet long and hundreds of feet wide. Then the earth would pour vast volumes of its molten guts out onto the landscape.

We use the word "catastrophic" far too readily these days when describing natural events; but in this instance it's not hyperbole. There would be 26 of these lava flows— collectively known as the Imnaha Group— and each of them would be catastrophic in every sense of the word. In the end they would entomb more than 20,000 square miles of the Pacific Northwest under almost 16,000 cubic miles of basalt. As horrific as they may have been, they were merely the first in a series of six[9] related volcanic events known as the Columbia River Flood Basalt Province or the Columbia River Basalts Group (CRBG).

The second round of CRBG events began almost before the smoke from the Imnaha eruptions had cleared away. Also centered in the far northeast portion of Oregon, the 120 eruptions that make up the Grande Ronde Group produced floods of lava so hot, so fast-moving, and so voluminous that a substantial portion of it reached the Pacific Ocean, approximately 350 miles away.

The Imnaha and Grande Ronde basalts were laid down in rapid succession, with little time between episodes for significant erosion or redevelopment of soils, or any of the other earmarks of a healed terrain. Altogether, the 146 eruptions involved spanned 1.5 million years, a mere blink of the eye in a geological context. They were also the most extensive of the CRBG outpourings. The Grande Ronde Group alone accounted for upwards of 60 percent of the total flow produced by the province. Bishop[10] estimates that this flow produced enough material to "construct a 7-foot thick, 100-foot wide basalt freeway to the moon."

Other outpourings would follow, but in far smaller volumes and at a far slower rate. Still, by the time the eruptions associated with the CRBG came to an end around 6 million years ago, 63,000 square miles of Oregon, Washington and

9 Steens, Imnaha, Grande Ronde, Picture Gorge, Wanapum and Saddle Mountain groups.
10 Bishop, E. (2003)

Idaho (an area larger than the state of Illinois) were buried beneath a blanket of lava up to three miles deep. In some places the flows had pooled to such an extent that the underlying surface of the planet was pushed down by as much as 1000 feet. The flows that made it to the sea tended to follow the ancient bed of the Columbia River. As a result, some of the basalts were deposited in the upper Willamette Valley and its adjoining areas, including what is now the Tualatin Basin. The Fanno Creek watershed sits on top of this basalt basement.

Even as the Grande Ronde flows were working their way across the northwest corner of the state and burying the once vibrant countryside under a thick blanket of lava, great engines deep within their smoldering masses were reshaping raw materials into the bones of a landscape that would ultimately produce the Fanno Creek watershed. Faulting, folding, buckling—the depths of the earth danced, and the surface above heaved and stretched until it bent or broke, fashioning slabs of rock into a grotesque and empty landscape. Other engines, including organic and inorganic processes, began tearing down the landscape almost from the instant it was formed. Many forces participated in this process, but water in all its forms was the chief architect and the primary tool.

Exposed to the elements, the still smoldering lava began to crack in innumerable microscopic places as the surface cooled too fast for the expanding interior to keep pace. Torrents of rain, highly acidic at first, swept across the land, etching the stone, collecting in countless depressions and cracks, and periodically freezing hard enough to break the now solid rock apart. Tiny granules of windblown rock and minerals picked up from one broken section scoured the surface and collected in the cracks of another. The chemical and physical forces beating away at the naked landscape were relentless enough, but they were soon joined by another powerful force, one every bit as irresistible as the elements: Life in all its wondrous forms broke out across the landscape.

The exterior surfaces of the decaying Grande Ronde basalts provided one type of habitat for a host of specialized living things; the cracks within them provided another. These life forms were not merely passive residents; they actively hastened the conversion of the basalt, first into clay and ultimately into soil. The layers of soil became deeper and richer every year. Before long, at least within a geological context, the dead, stone-face of the land had once again been clothed with a flourishing blanket of plants and animals. A period of relative peace and tranquility persisted for almost four million years. Then all hell broke loose once again, this time near the site of Boring, Oregon. This new round of volcanic activity would ultimately create the northeastern rim of the Fanno Creek watershed.

Bone Yard

There isn't a square inch of the Fanno Creek watershed that hasn't been clear-cut, dug up and turned over at least once in the last 150 years. There are, however, a few areas that haven't been messed with very much since the late 1960s. Most of these places lie in deep ravines that cleave the Tualatin Hills, the ridge of low mountains forming the northern and eastern rims of the watershed. The vast majority of these ravines were first gutted sometime between 1920 and 1960 in order to lay the pipes (water, gas and sewage) and electrical lines needed to make neighborhood living the luxury it is today.

Once the utilities were in place, the ravines were allowed to return to nature. Their slopes were too steep and unstable to be of much use for anything else. From time to time, utility crews visit these places in order to clear away brush from sewer inspection towers or to perform other kinds of routine maintenance. Otherwise, human incursion into these places is rare, and they are so overgrown with vegetation that a considerable amount of determined bushwhacking is required to explore them. Game is usually abundant in such places.[11] I've encountered deer, skunks, opossums, rats, bats, squirrels, feral cats and coyotes. A wide variety of birds hang out in these ravines as well, including Stellar jays and pileated woodpeckers.

These heavily overgrown areas are invariably dominated by the worst kinds of invasive plants—English ivy, Himalayan blackberry and non-native hawthorn, to name just a few. Fortunately, these ravines are generally free of the kinds of pollution that normally clutter the marginal areas of commercial and residential developments. A stream typically runs along the bottom of the ravine, often a perennial one with a name. When folks talk about a "natural area" within the urban watershed context, most often this is the kind of place they have in mind.

It was in one of these dark and quiet places that I first encountered the Boring basalts.[12] I had entered the ravine at a culvert and was slowly making my way up a streambed that was ankle-deep with water and knee-deep with rocks. Forward progress was hard, but I was thrilled to have found an area so clearly "untouched." From time to time passage up the streambed would be blocked by the fallen carcass of a large tree. Sometimes I could crawl under the blockage on my hands and knees. At other times I had to abandon the creek altogether and bushwhack my way around to the other side. The trees in this ravine were mostly Douglas firs, many of a good size. Most of the fallen ones had been down

11 In 2002 elk were sighted multiple times in an area of SW Portland where several major Fanno Creek tributaries carry water off the northern elevations of the West Slope. SWNI (2007)
12 USGS (2011).

Boring basalts "natural area" flourishing on the slopes of an old volcano

quite a while. Their broken branches were devoid of needles and the splintered places were a dull gray. Despite all the downed wood, the canopy above was still tight.

A quarter-mile into my crawl I pushed through a wall of chest-high salal and entered a clearing roughly forty feet long and twenty feet wide. The character of the streambed changed dramatically. The tumbled rocks that had littered the channel were replaced by a relatively flat, gray plate of solid rock. There was a slight diagonal pitch to the ground which pushed the stream into a narrow channel along the west side of an overhanging embankment. The up-slope half of the exposed rock was covered in a thick mat of moss and sprinkled with detritus. The other half had been scoured clean by the action of the stream during recent heavy rains Considerable incising had occurred between the down-slope side of the plate and the embankment: all the soils and vegetation once part of the streambed had been stripped away, up to a high-water mark of about two feet. That erosion had exposed the edge of another expanse of rock that appeared to be folded over the first. Except for a few stray roots from some of the bushes on the top of this second rocky mass, the soil had been undercut to such an extent that the vegetated ground above lay on the bare rock like a bad toupee perched on a bald head. A few fist-sized, water-rounded gray rocks stuck out of the mud below the edges of the toupee. I pulled a couple of them out and broke one open with my rock hammer.

The blow split the egg-shaped rock almost perfectly in half. I couldn't have done much better if I'd been using a saw. Long immersion in the clay had stained the exterior surface a dark reddish brown. Just beneath this stained layer the interior of the rock was a deep, bluish gray color. A few millimeters closer to the center, the tone of the material brightened a bit but the color itself remained a cool gray. I figured that the darker shell was a sign that the material was water friendly, at least up to a point. The interior texture of the broken rock was similar to 60-grit sandpaper, but under a magnifier it appeared to be much coarser, with more sharply-edged grains. Tiny, green-tinted crystals were scattered uniformly throughout the interior of the rock. Olivine, I guessed, and concluded that the rock slabs in this ravine had been laid down by one or more of the eruptions that took place in this area as recently as 500,000 years ago.

There's an old saying around these parts: You know you live in Portland when (1) all the Honda Civics have gun racks in the back; (2) all the old hippies tell you their neighbors are weird; and (3) there's a live volcano in your backyard. The volcano referred to in this old saw is a square-mile sized cinder cone named Mount Tabor. It's a *dormant* volcano, which means it is anything but dead and could "go big" someday in the future. However, residential neighborhoods and commercial enterprises have been built right up to the lower flanks of the cone.

Mt. Tabor is one of at least 32 cinder cones and shield volcanoes that began erupting across the central and eastern portions of the Portland Basin about 2.7 million years ago. Most of these eruptions took place near what is now the suburb of Boring, Oregon—hence the name for the province.[13] However, a half dozen or more of them erupted west of downtown Portland. The pyrotechnics associated with these volcanoes came to a close in the Fanno Creek area half a million years ago, but the shaping of the creek's basin was anything but finished.

Even before the Boring eruptions blew holes through them, the Grande Ronde Basalts that form the basement of the Tualatin Basin were being rearranged by non-stop seismic events, many of them of enormous magnitude.

On top of this dynamic landscape, layer upon layer of ultra-fine material[14] blew into the area, accumulating to a depth of 40 feet in many areas. Life in one form or another has never been absent from this violent landscape for very long. When the materials for soil became sufficiently abundant, the red tops of the mountains vanished beneath thick blankets of vegetation. Ancient Fanno Creek ran clean and strong through the virgin landscape and into the Tualatin River.

Then, 15,000 years ago, yet another cataclysm hit the Pacific Northwest. This time the killer was water in almost unimaginable quantities, a flood of truly biblical proportions. And when the world ended this time, someone may have been left alive to weep over it.

Bad Day at Dry Falls

In the early 1990s I began exploring the eastern portions of Washington and Oregon. The "Dry Side" it's called, and for good reason. The Cascade Mountain Range acts like a giant wall, keeping those eastern areas rain-free for all but a short period of the year. I rode a motorcycle in those days, a BMW k-75 built for the long-haul. On one of my first trips to the Dry Side I encountered a geological wonder that moved me to the bottom of my boots.

It was mid-August and hot. I'd ridden east out of Wenatchee and across the Waterville Plateau on blue highways so empty and smooth that at times I must have actually flown. I stopped once at the boarded-up grange in Farmer, resting on the bike for 15 minutes while I washed down a package of peanut butter and cheese crackers with some lukewarm, black coffee. Then I pulled the bike back

---

13 "A geological province is any large area or region considered as a whole, all parts of which are characterized by similar features or by a history differing significantly from that of adjacent areas." USGS (2012)
14 Loess from post-glaciated plains to the north and the east.

onto the highway and sped east, letting up on the throttle again only when the road twisted its way through a wide, dropping turn at Moses Coulee. Twenty miles later the highway began its steep descent down the leading edge of the Withrow Moraine. This collection of shattered rocks and powdery soil marks the most southerly advance of the Okanogan Lobe of the Cordilleran Glacier, the massive sheet of ice that ultimately led to the creation of the Grand Coulee and all that came with it.

At the base of the moraine lies the junction of Highway 2 and Highway 17. If you go straight here, you head towards the Grand Coulee Dam, another 30 miles to the east. But I was butt-weary and needed a stretch, so when I saw the sign for the Dry Falls Interpretive Center I headed south down 17, figuring that there might be a clean restroom and maybe a scrap of shade where I could have some lunch. I had no idea what Dry Falls was, but judging from the desolate landscape stretching out in every direction, it couldn't be much. I parked the bike in what little shade I could find, pulled a warm bologna sandwich and a Coke out of my saddle bag, and sauntered over to a nearby rock wall to see what the several people standing there were gawking about. I looked over the edge and nearly dropped my sandwich.

Dry Falls is a 385-foot-deep hole gouged out of an immense plateau that stretches east and south as far as the eye can see. At the visitor center the gash is half a mile wide and more than three miles long. A legend posted on a nearby post explained that this hole had been torn out of solid rock by a flood so massive that the place where I stood had once been under 300 feet of water. I looked back across the wide open expanse, toward a band of dark clouds on the northeastern horizon. What had been a strong and steady breeze dropped off to nothing, leaving a stillness that made my ears ring. Through the ringing I could just discern a lower-frequency rumble from somewhere in the distance. The small hairs on the back of my neck stood up, and I strained to see if anything was moving out there on the horizon. The pitch and volume of the deep throbbing sound increased rapidly. So did the beating of my heart. Seconds later, high drama was turned to farce when a southbound dump truck roared past the center. Still, for a moment I had been transported back to an incredible place in time and space. In my imagination I had stood witness to one of the most spectacular events in prehistory. And while I don't usually believe in ghosts, I could have sworn that somewhere in that violent, rumbling sound I had heard a human voice speaking in a strange language.

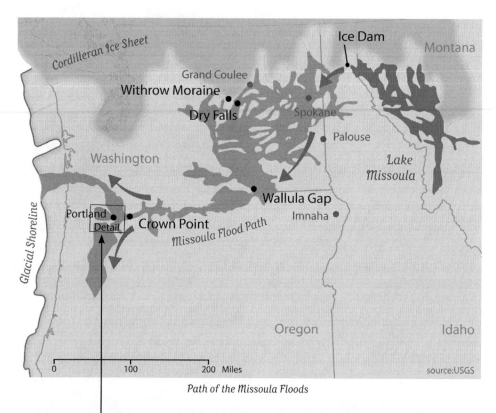

Path of the Missoula Floods

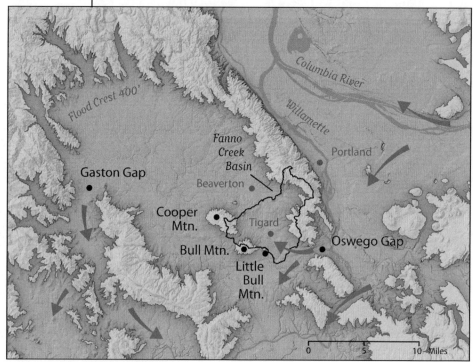

The Great Flood

Fifteen thousand years ago the Cordilleran ice sheet that deposited the Withrow Moraine a few hundred yards west of Dry Falls had moved south into Washington and Idaho far enough to block the ancestral courses of both the Columbia and Clark Fork rivers. The damming of the Columbia created ancient Lake Columbia and diverted the river, first into the Grand Coulee, then into the Moses Coulee, 20 miles to the west . These diversions were spectacular, but they were minor compared to the lake that developed from the damming of the Clark Fork River, a hundred miles further east.

The Clark Fork flows westward out of Montana and into Idaho. Its progress is bounded by the Bitterroot Range to the south and the Cabinet Range to the north. When one of the lobes[15] along the leading edge of the ice sheet crunched into the Bitterroots and dammed the river, ancient Lake Missoula was formed. Other nearby glacial activity slowly cut off any overflow through the lower mountain valleys to the north. In time the lake grew to an enormous size.

The dam was huge. Some estimates put it at 2,500 feet high and 30 miles across.[16] Behind it were more than 530 cubic miles of water, roughly the same amount in Lake Erie and Lake Ontario combined. Multiple theories attempt to explain how the dam failed. The simplest posits that it floated off the bedrock for a split second when the water behind it reached the level of 2,500 feet. With its base destabilized, and with one or more of its wings or facings breached, the dam failed instantaneously and catastrophically.[17] Within seconds a torrent of water more than a mile across and a thousand feet high took off across the prairie at 70 miles per hour.

As the flood escaped into the open landscape to the west it began to spread out and get shallower, but the leading edge was still more than 400 feet high when it cut through the Spokane area and began ravaging the Palouse. Less than an hour later, still moving at speeds up to 50 miles per hour, the wall plowed into Glacial Lake Columbia. The impact sent a huge wave of water surging into the north end of Grand Coulee. It was more water than the Coulee could handle. The floodwaters were still 300 feet high when they stormed out of the Coulee and headed south. Seconds later, boulders and gravel caught up in cyclonic turbulence along the bottom of the flood had carved out the gigantic, rock-cut basin that is Dry Falls today.

From Dry Falls the floodwaters continued south, tearing up the ground and adjacent hillsides for almost a hundred miles until they reached the Wallula Gap. The Gap is the only natural outlet for the entire eastern portion of the Columbia Basin. It's big, almost a mile wide, and nearly a thousand feet deep. Still,

15 The Purcell Lobe.
16 Allen, Burns & Burns (2009).
17 Lee (2008)

it was far too small for the entire flood to pass through all at once, so a hydraulic dam developed. This slowed the passage of the flood and in the process created Lake Lewis, a 5,043 square-mile impoundment that remained for more than a week as the floodwaters drained through the Gap and headed towards the Columbia River Gorge.

Much of the character of the Columbia Gorge today stems from the dramatic impact of the Missoula Floods. In the narrowest places of the Gorge the deluge was so constricted that the flow may have reached speeds of over 50 miles per hour. In some places the water crested at more than 1000 feet. It's likely that the leading edge of the flood reached the narrows at Crown Point less than 18 hours after the explosion of the dam in Montana, almost 350 miles away.[18]

When it passed Crown Point and exploded out of the Gorge, the wall of water was over 400 feet high and a mile wide. The water column behind it was more than 200 miles long. Suspended within it were millions of tons of shattered ice, boulders, sand, and pebbles. Softer materials, such as animal carcasses and trees, had been reduced to an organic froth. For a few minutes the flow surged through the Columbia's floodplain and headed north towards the narrows at Kalama. There, the passage was too constricted to allow more than a portion of the flood to pass. This created another hydraulic dam that backed up the main flow until finally it spilled out of the floodplain and headed south into the Portland Basin. Only a third of the floodwaters went in this direction, yet the volume was enough to fill the entire Willamette Basin and most of its side valleys all the way to what is now Eugene, Oregon, a hundred miles away.[19] The Tualatin Valley, home to Fanno Creek, was one of the first and hardest hit of these side valleys.

Before the flood could flow out of the south end of the Portland Basin and into the Willamette Valley, it had to work its way through the narrow canyon where the Willamette River drained into its namesake valley. The constriction here was sufficient to force the first surge of flood water back upon itself. For a few minutes the frustrated waters must have raged away in considerable fury. But four miles to the north the recoiling waters found a place where they could escape into the west.

Today the Lake Oswego Gap holds a 400-acre, man-made lake surrounded by expensive homes. Fifteen thousand years ago, the area was an upland bench formed by the confluence of lava flows that had spilled out of Mount Sylvania and Cook's Butte during the Boring eruptions. Its exact elevation is unknown,

18 The elevation at the dam was around 4,000 feet above sea level. The elevation at Crown Point is around 40 feet today.
19 Lake Allison was 3,000 sq. mi. in area. When the Portland Basin was fully flooded the water was 400 feet deep.

but the Gap was probably no more than 150 feet above the floor of the Portland Basin when the floodwaters surged in. They quickly overtopped the bench,
then ripped through the Gap and into the Tualatin Basin.

Two massive hills sit in a line just inside the entrance to the Tualatin Basin:
Bull Mountain and Cooper Mountain. Nearly contiguous, these hills represented a square mile of immovable object to the flood's otherwise irresistible force.
The incoming crest plowed into the south end of Bull Mountain and split into
two distinct flows.[20] The first sped off to the northwest, generally following the
ancestral bed of the Tualatin River. Minutes later it broke out into the Tualatin
Basin. From there the surging waters met few obstacles until they crashed into
the foothills of the Pacific Coast Range, almost twenty miles away.

The second flow went north, straight up the Fanno Creek channel. This offered a shorter, but somewhat more torturous, route into the main portion
of the basin. One of the more significant obstacles in its path was Little Bull
Mountain, a 420-foot knob at the southeastern end of Bull Mountain. On its way
in, the flood scoured all but the uppermost elevations of this promontory down
to bedrock. Overcoming this obstacle robbed the surging waters of a portion
of their energy. Heavier materials, including some just ripped away from the
knob itself, began settling out along the lee side of the knob.

The rest of the Fanno Creek sub-basin offered little resistance. The flood
moved rapidly north through this corridor, out onto the main floor of the basin,
where its waters re-mingled with those flowing in from the west side of Cooper
Mountain. The inundation went on for days, until finally the entire basin was
filled to a level of 350 feet. The newly formed lake covered an area of more than
250 square miles. The tops of Bull and Cooper mountains were now islands surrounded by water that was filled with chunks of ice and other debris. In the
western end of the basin, where the floodwaters may have pooled in relative
tranquility for several months, the flood deposited deep layers of some of the
highest quality soils in North America. Much of the settlement of the Oregon
Territory was driven by the fertility of these soils. Then, as now, they represented one of Oregon's most important natural resources.

It is unclear how long the waters lay on the land before they began to recede,
but it could have been several weeks before the floor of the basin began to reap-
pear. While the process was relatively gradual and gentle in some areas, it was
chaotic in others. The receding waters departed through four areas: the Gaston
Gap (the northwestern portion of the basin); the Tonquin Scablands (the previ-

20 A third flow split off from the main inundation only after the incoming water over-topped the Tualatin
River's floodplains and surrounding uplands. It pushed south through an area known today as the Tonquin
Scablands and into the upper end of the Willamette Valley.

ously noted southern route); the Tualatin Gap (the new course of the Tualatin River); and the Lake Oswego Gap (the flood's main entryway). The turbulence in these relatively confined spaces was extreme, which added significantly to the stirring and ultimate redistribution of materials carried by the flood during its entrance and egress.

A substantial portion of the basin's outflow passed through the Fanno Creek watershed. Once again floodwaters surged over and around Little Bull Mountain. This time, however, the knob acted as a compression dam. Lighter materials began to collect along the north side of the knob, burying the boulders, rocks, gravels and sands that had been deposited there by the incoming flood.

Eventually the floodwaters receded and the floor of the ravaged basin began to heal. Only the most scoured areas remained totally naked for long, and soon even these were sporting brand-new garments of green. The upper reaches of Fanno Creek had been left intact and now served as a nursery for the waves of new life moving down from the hills and onto the basin floor. In time the watershed returned to something like its pre-deluge self. It's even possible that a few Paleo-people came into the basin at that time. If they did, humans may have witnessed the arrival of a second flood of similar or even more extreme proportions. Lake Missoula refilled and failed repeatedly over the next 3,000 years. There were at least 40 such outpourings, and at least 30[21] of them would have been sufficiently large to rival the one described here.

The water from the last of these catastrophic events drained out of the Fanno Creek watershed by 11,000 BCE. Even before the floor of the basin was completely dry, a low area on a ridge of compacted debris less than a mile northeast of Little Bull Mountain filled to overflowing with rain water. Down the hill the water went, towards the main stem of Fanno Creek, just over a mile away. Suspended within its little column were microscopic chunks of Montana, Idaho, Washington and the rim-rock around Dry Falls. Water filled and overflowed from a second depression along the next rise to the north, and eventually the two joined to form a more robust body of water. A creek was born and one day it would have a lovely name.

Derry Dell Creek

Carla Staedter was one of the first Watershed Folk I met when I began studying Fanno Creek. Watershed Folk aren't like you and me. Without them the rest of us would be far less well-off than we are. Yet most of the time they go about their business without most of us ever knowing about the role they play in increasing our long term odds of survival. These folks generally share the following characteristics:

21 O'connor & Costa (2012)

- engaged formally or otherwise in the actual management of a watershed.
- committed to protecting and enhancing the biological integrity of the watershed.
- oriented towards a watershed approach to problem-solving.

I met Carla at her office in Tigard. She's the Surface Water Quality/Volunteer Coordinator for Tigard's Public Works Division. You need to be in the watershed management business to understand what's involved when you see the word "coordinator" in a title. A coordinator's activities range across a spectrum beginning with a ton of basic phone work and ending with on-the-ground management of outdoor activities that may involve several hundred people.[22] People like Carla establish and maintain collaborative relationships with the disparate groups typically involved in a city's efforts to manage its natural resources—agencies, other governments, environmental groups and educational institutions, to name just a few.

She brought me up to speed on some of the wetlands projects the city was working on, then suggested we take a look at an area where the city was wrapping up some major restoration work. As we drove to the site she talked about some of the watershed groups she worked with. I would need to learn about those groups, she told me, before I went much further in my study. I already knew a little about some of them, particularly the regulatory organizations like the Corps of Engineers, the Environmental Protection Agency (EPA) and the Oregon Department of Environmental Quality (DEQ). But then Carla started talking about outreach and education groups I had never heard of. I was feverishly taking notes even as we were getting out of her car. She laughed. "Don't worry," she said, "I'll email you the information later. This is Derry Dell. Let's walk."

I'd originally given this creek a low priority when I was setting up my research agenda. For one thing, it isn't named on most maps, nor is it very long. From its confluence with Fanno Creek to Gaarde Street (its nominal headwaters area) the main stem of the creek is just over a mile long. The highest elevation along Gaarde is 320 feet, which places the upper reaches of its watershed at only 170 feet higher than its confluence with Fanno Creek. Until Carla informed me that we were going to walk a major portion of its corridor, I didn't know the creek was accessible. According to my maps, the creek was jammed into an incredibly tight corridor running through the backyards of dozens of homes. I'd thought that corridor was too constricted to provide room for even a narrow path.

---

22 Later in our relationship I watched Carla manage a restoration planting event in one of the wetlands that feed Fanno Creek. Called a Tree For All, the event involved well over a hundred volunteers and a couple dozen support personnel. Volunteers had to be equipped, trained and monitored as they went about the task of planting more than 2,000 wetland plants and trees in something under four hours. The entire event went off flawlessly.

The stream corridor was narrow indeed. Where the paved pathway began, the width of the stream corridor was less than fifty feet from backyard fence to backyard fence. The streambed proper was also very narrow, no more than eight feet from one bank top to the other. As we walked, Carla downloaded a continuous stream of information. Most of Tigard's major watershed projects were collaborations with Clean Water Services (cws), she said; but this one was a solo effort by the city. She didn't say that cws had been uninterested in the project, but I couldn't imagine this little stream ranking high in the consideration of an agency charged with managing waste and stormwater quality needs for an area half the size of a small state.

Carla nodded in silent agreement, but pointed out that from a watershed perspective, even a body of water as small and ephemeral as this one played a key role in the overall health of the watershed. She pointed at a gravelly area just downstream from a small bend in the creek.

"Ever seen a Pacific lamprey? They spawn in this creek and are an indicator species, one of the 'canaries in the mine shaft'. When this stream is clean and flowing properly, this is ideal habitat for them. That's one of the reasons we're going to the trouble of restoring habitat in here."

I asked her about the restoration process—what were the most valuable lessons learned? She started laughing.

"I began work on this site when I was still learning the restoration ropes, and I learned a lot of valuable lessons, not so much about plantings and stream regimes and such, but mostly about communications. One of the first steps in the implementation of projects like the one on Derry Dell involves the wholesale removal of the non-native species that have escaped into the stream corridor. Blackberries, ivy, non-native hawthorn, bamboo, laurel. All of it had to go before any of the actual restoration could take place," she said. "So one morning the neighbors woke up, looked out their backyard windows and saw...each other!"

That was a couple of years ago, and in some places the vegetation had still not fully recovered. It was still an issue for some of the residents. A handful of folks had bought into the idea of fixing up the stream corridor and were actively removing invasive species from their own yards, but many more remained uninvolved. I pointed out that some neighbors appeared to be actively thwarting the restoration process by dumping cuttings, grass clippings and even old Christmas trees into the area. Carla just shook her head.

"When you work in this business for a while, nothing like this ever surprises you, and eventually it doesn't even make you very angry. Most people operate on the mistaken notion that this kind of 'bio-degradable material' is actually beneficial to the land. They don't see it as refuse. They see it as a kind of fertilizer. If you call them on it, they're genuinely surprised. That kind of misinformation is why the outreach and education sides of my job are so important."

We came to the place where the stream forks into two branches. The pathway veered off to the northwest, and as we moved further up the hillside the stream way expanded and the vegetation became more robust. Some of the alders in this reach were as large as a foot in diameter, but most were much smaller. Occasionally we passed a larger tree, usually an ash or a big leaf maple. Invariably these were located on the margins of the residential properties. All the trees, with the exception of the youngest alder saplings had bows in their trunks. These bows are land movement tell-tales; that they were evident, even in many of the younger trees, underscored the fact that the land beneath our feet is moving all the time.

I was mulling this over when we came to an area where the stream had cut a pair of channels more than six feet deep into the muddy creek bed. I looked at Carla, who nodded agreement. "Very unstable," she said. She was concerned about this area and a second one just ahead, where erosion and the land movement were serious enough to require intervention.

"There's more concrete up here than treetop, so when it rains hard the creek cuts deeper into the main channel until it hits bedrock. Then it moves out left and right and cuts deeper into the softer stuff lying on top of the hardpan or bedrock. After a while, the hillside is undercut enough to cave in. That fills the channel with a brand-new batch of very loose material, which it moves out of the system the way the conveyor belt at the grocery store moves your soup cans.

"As the creek moves the loose material out of the system, it's also increasing the width, and sometimes even the depth, of the channel. It does this to some extent every time a good rain comes along. This is not good news for the stability of the slopes." She gestured towards the houses perched along the rim and frowned. "It could be especially bad news for them."

On the way back to the car Carla talked about the Missoula Floods. "Most of the soil instability in this area is left over from those floods. There wasn't just one, you know. More like dozens of them. Every time they came into this area they stirred things up even more. So there's a very challenging mix of soils in the lower ravines all along Bull Mountain." Suddenly she stopped walking, bent down and picked up a rock. She eyed it critically for a moment, then tossed it into the creek. "Darn!" She grinned. "I thought it might be an arrow head. You know about the Indians that lived here before the settlers came, don't you? The valley was named after them."

Camas, essential root-food and economic mainstay of the Atfalati economy

3—Children of the Flood

Storyteller

For an hour the Coos-Atfalati[23] storyteller carried the audience firmly but gently with her voice as she weaved her way through an ancient world populated with mythical characters. Coyote, Snake Man and Crow Woman all came to life in the spaces between her words. Each had important lessons for us to learn. Almost from the instant she began to speak I was lifted off the cold seat of my folding chair and propelled through space and time. The stories were earthy, sometimes even a little ribald, yet something in the storyteller's voice created a sense of ethereal beauty. When she came to the end and invited questions from the audience I felt for a moment or two as if I had just woken from a dream. There was a pause, then hands went up all around the room. She answered everyone in generous detail before her sparkling eyes finally met mine. "Esther," I asked, "Would you tell us a story about the Flood?"

I knew almost from the instant the words left my lips that I had somehow transgressed. Her eyes darkened. The smile that had flickered around the corners of her lips for more than an hour evaporated. The air of animation and excitement that had gripped her entire being suddenly vanished. Her shoulders relaxed for a second. Then her posture, already erect and dignified, became decidedly more so. It was clear that the storytelling had ended and a different kind of schooling was about to begin.

"No, I won't. That is not one of the stories I tell in public. Some stories can't be told except at certain ceremonies or at certain times of the year. For example, I do not tell stories about Bear in the winter because the strong power in the story could wake him from his hibernation. I have only 13 stories that are for the public. The rest are private property."

She placed no particular emphasis on the phrase "private property," but her meaning was clear. I almost flinched at her words, feeling as chagrined, chastised and diminished as any Indian child might have, had he behaved as rudely to the storyteller as I. I shook her hand as we left the meeting. It was warm and firm, but it didn't linger in my clasp. Her eyes looked directly into mine; the twinkle had returned, but they were as unfathomable as a starlit night. She had distanced herself from me by at least a thousand years.

I felt no resentment, just deep disappointment and more than a little remorse. At first I wasn't sure how I had transgressed, but I was certain the fault was mine. After a little reflection it came to me: I had been too impatient and

23 The word Atfalati was corrupted by Euro-Americans first into Tuality and then into Tualatin. Throughout this section I use Atfalati for the people to avoid potential confusion between references to them and their namesake valley.

self-absorbed to ask such a question without giving offense. I had ignored her station, as well as my own. Worse still, I had unceremoniously and publicly asked her to violate a taboo. I could be forgiven the self-absorption, I decided, and maybe even the ignorant encroachment on the taboo; but the total lack of ceremony was unforgivable and I knew it.

Still, the encounter had not been a total loss. I had heard her voice and had felt the power of the myths she'd related. Next to a people's art, nothing conveys the subtleties of their lived experience better than their mythology.[24] I hadn't expected the storyteller to channel up a survivor from the Missoula Floods, but in her tales I had heard an echo from a village of similar antiquity. Those sounds, combined with her nearly magical presence, more than compensated for not being allowed to hear the story of the Flood from someone whose distant ancestors may have seen it with their own eyes. I was ready, finally, to bring to a close my study of Atfalati—the remarkable people who first stepped onto the banks of Fanno Creek.

For over a year I had been digging into the story of these Indians, the first recorded settlers in the Tualatin Valley. The archeological record is sketchy at best. The most authoritative resources are maddeningly incomplete and often couched in the most conditional language possible. The more I learned about any aspect of the Indian experience, the less prepared I was to say I knew anything certain about their remarkable saga. Here is a sample of what I had been working on. The author is describing the location of *Chachiamahiuk (sha-shee-ahmahee-hook)*, an Atfalati winter settlement once located within the Fanno Creek watershed.[25]

> More or less definitely identified.... Probably located somewhere south of Beaverton, near the Tualatin River. There is an element of confusion in the location, Gatschet originally giving it as "near Oregon City" and writing "Wappato [sic] lake." However, the location is elsewhere given as "between Oregon City and Chehalem (i.e., west or southwest of Oregon City, 'Chehalem' presumably referring to the vicinity of Chehalem Valley...(Zenk, 1976)[26]

Zenk's indecisiveness was understandable. We know more about the origins and subsequent movements of the rocks in Oregon than we do about the humans who first walked on them. There's simply not much hard evidence left to go on.

24 Campbell (1991)
25 See section on Augustus Fanno
26 When the author says "element of confusion" he isn't kidding. Oregon City is ten miles southeast of Beaverton; Lake Wapato is ten miles west of Beaverton; and the mouth of the Chehalem Valley lies at least ten miles to the south (and across the Tualatin River) from Beaverton.

Eye Witnesses

The same changes in climate that led to the breakup of the Clark Fork ice dam began to warm up and dry out large areas of the Pacific Northwest, including the Willamette and its sub-basins. As prevailing weather patterns in the Northwest continued shifting toward warmer conditions, the Pacific Ocean began to reclaim the miles of seafloor that had lain bare during the Ice Age.[27] Eventually the flora and fauna south of the Columbia River began to flourish. At some point one of the small, diverse groups of Paleo-Indians who already foraged the surrounding areas—the coastal lands to the west, the riverine environments to the north, and the Columbia Plateau to the east—ventured out of the uplands and onto the valley floor. Perhaps even as the waters from the last of the mega-floods were receding from the Tualatin Valley, some of these hunters were beginning to move through its forests and across its plain. Who were they? How did they get here? What routes did they follow as they penetrated the interior regions of the Pacific Northwest? Did they or their ancestors witness any of the deluges that shaped so many areas of the present-day Pacific Northwest?

There are no definitive answers to these questions. Geologists are still working out iron-clad dates for the floods, and anthropologists are engaged in similar debate about the timing of human incursions into this area. Still, a picture is emerging that suggests Paleo-Indians were well established in Oregon when the last of the great floods drained out of the Tualatin Basin. In 2003 a team of geologists[28] using radio-carbon dating techniques reported that at least twenty five mega-floods passed through the Portland Basin sometime between 12,000 and 15,000 years ago. Then, in 2007, researchers from the University of Oregon, working at one of the Paisley Caves archeological sites in south-central Oregon, found several pieces of fossilized human scat (coprolites) that date from around 14,500 years ago.[29] For now these remains represent the earliest evidence of human occupation of Oregon during a time frame that roughly overlaps at least the latest of the Missoula Floods to pass through the Portland area.

Multiple theories attempt to explain how the Paleo-people found their way into the Pacific Northwest:

One Route: The migrations took place across a land bridge (Beringia)[30] and down the western coast of North America when the glaciers took up enough of the planet's waters to lower the Pacific Ocean by more than 600 feet.

Two Routes: The migrations took place using the same land bridge, but instead of using only the coastal route the people also moved south through an

27 Madsen (2004)
28 Benito & O'Connor (2003). Only a few of these floods were as monumental as the one described in Chapter 2, but all would have been of relatively epic proportions.
29 Barlow (2012)
30 The sub-continent of Beringia was exposed when the formation of glaciers all across the northern portions of the continent took up enough water to expose the shallowest portions of the continental plate.

ice-free corridor that opened up along the eastern side of the Rockies.

Sea Route: Forget overland routes; the Indians came into America by canoe, then dispersed into the interior by moving up the many coastal rivers.

My choice: All, or parts of all of the above.

The Paisley Caves are situated 150 miles east of the Pacific Coast and 250 miles south of the Columbia River. They were inhabited almost continuously until shortly before the re-settlement of Oregon by Euro-Americans. Knowing where the first inhabitants of these caves came from might shed light on how and where other populations of Paleo-people were distributed throughout the rest of Oregon in the days immediately following the Missoula Floods. This knowledge could help determine which population of post-deluge Indians were the first to venture into the Tualatin Valley.

That population might have been the ancestors of the resourceful Chinooks, ultimately the most populous and powerful native peoples in this portion of the Northwest. They controlled virtually all access to the Columbia from the mouth of the river all the way to The Dalles. All of it, that is, except for a small section of the southern shore. That portion was controlled by the Clatskanie,[31] a small but very fierce band of Indians. From a map of their range developed by Cressman (1981) it appears that they must have been wrangling constantly with the Chinooks. The Columbia River fish runs figured largely in the scheme of their subsistence, but the Clatskanie probably relied equally on the plentiful game in their section of the Coastal Range. They were reputed to be skilled hunters and fierce warriors. The mountains they roamed were heavily forested and extended south-southeast all the way to the upper areas of the Tualatin Basin.

Whoever the first Indians to explore the Tualatin Basin may have been, it's generally agreed that the first to settle it permanently were members of an extended family whose closest ties were with the Kalapuya. They called themselves the Atfalati, and though they were initially small in number they would leave an indelible mark upon the virgin landscape.

Acorns to Oak Trees

It took the Willamette Valley, particularly its northernmost basins, a long time to recover from the devastation wrought by multiple mega-floods. But recover they did, and with a bounty that remains one of the most spectacular in North America. The millions of tons of loess and other rich soils ripped out of Washington, then deposited across the floor of the Tualatin Valley, ensured that when the land finally began to heal, the process would be phenomenal and rapid.[32]

The Kalapuya Indians took possession of this breadbasket between nine and twelve thousand years ago. They remained in control until diseases

31 Minor et al (1980)

32 A geologist friend of mine once quipped, "Yup, Washington's loess turned out to be Oregon's grain."

brought into the land by Euro-Americans killed off all but a handful of them in the early 1800s. Exactly where these Indians came from is unknown but it's likely their ancestors moved inland along the Umpqua River, settling for a time in the mountain valleys south of the Willamette Basin. The Kalapuya pushed their range ever northward, following in a general sort of way the expanding bounty of the valley floor, until they finally reached the areas controlled by the Chinook Indians and their close relatives the Clackamas. These Chinookian peoples controlled the Columbia River and most of the Portland Basin. Where the first encounters among the Kalapuya, Chinooks and Clackamas took place is unknown, but it was most likely in the area just south of the Willamette Falls.

The Chinookians were well known for being militant when it came to protecting their fishing and hunting resources; but they were equally well known for being shrewd businessmen. For their part, the Kalapuya were every bit as fierce and well-armed as the Chinookians, although probably not so numerous, and didn't end up controlling the bulk of the Willamette Valley and its side valleys by accident.[33] Still, while conflict was inevitable, open and protracted warfare was not. The Willamette Falls wasn't the only prized resource in the area. Just a few miles south of the falls two rivers flowed out of virgin territories to the west and met the Willamette River. The Yamhill River, southernmost of the two, took its name from the band of Kalapuya that ventured up its fish- and game-filled valleys and made them their own. A second and closely related Kalapuya band, the Atfalati, moved up the northernmost river valley and took control of a vast plain blessed with soils and other natural resources rivaling those in the rest of the Willamette Valley.

Exactly when the Atfalati took up residence in the Tualatin Valley is not known. Estimates range from 4,000 to 9,000 years ago.[34] Whatever the case may have been, they prospered and their population grew until they became the most numerous of the Kalapuyan bands. Like the other bands, the Atfalati were "affluent foragers"[35], complex hunter-gathers with a culture that differed from that of more traditional hunter-gatherers in several important ways:

The Atfalati stayed put, not just within a well-defined territory, but in relatively fixed locations within that territory. Their villages might stand on the same piece of land for many years. Their seasonal hunts were conducted in well-defined forest areas, and they controlled the hunting rights there, passing them to the next generation and possibly using them to barter.

33 At their peak the Kalapuya may have numbered 15,000.
34 A paper by O,Neill, Connolly & Freidel (2004) covering two archaeological sites in the Upper Willamette Valley places humans in the area as early as 10,000 years ago. These older finds are described as "ephemeral." More concentrated use of the same sites dates to roughly 5,000 years ago.
35 Ames and Maschner, 1999

Unlike their counterparts on the Plains, they built walled houses from a variety of materials, including red cedar planks and bark, as well as the bark and poles from Oregon ash. These were solid and long-lasting structures.

Like more traditional foragers, the Atfalati capitalized on any readily available food resource. However, they also developed a wide range of secondary food resources, several of which required considerable group effort and communication to exploit.

Atfalati economy was based on the ability of the band to collect, process, and store large quantities of primary and secondary food resources. As part of the underlying structure of these economic activities, families held ownership of specific plots of resources—tarweed[36] sites, for example. Like hunting territories, these plots were handed down from generation to generation.

An outgrowth of living in one spot for year after year is an accumulation of what George Carlin once referred to as "stuff." For the Atfalati, "stuff" amounted to beds, mats, storage containers, specialized cooking apparatus, and utensils too sophisticated to fit the more traditional hunter-gatherer paradigm. They also accumulated specialized technology and gear related to hunting and food gathering.

Populations and population densities related to complex hunter-gatherer societies tend to run higher than those of the more traditional hunter-gatherer groups. At their peak the Kalapuya numbered between 14,000 and 20,000. The Atfalati may have accounted for more than a quarter of this number.

When a group of people moves from a nomadic state to a more sedentary one, the inevitable result is an increase in organizational complexity. This leads to increased complexity of social interactions at the functional and symbolic levels. Some specialization of roles may exist in nomadic societies, but in sedentary populations it becomes more pervasive and formalized. In addition, nomadic groups tend to react to their environments and exercise little direct control over them. Affluent foraging societies, on the other hand, tend to be more proactive, taking control over key aspects of their environment through coordinated group action and the use of sophisticated technology.[37] Nowhere is this last point more evident than in the degree to which the Atfalati and the other Kalapuya bands controlled the productivity of their lands. At some point in their history they either invented or acquired a land management regime that brought several key production processes of the environment firmly under their control. Their principle technology was fire.[38]

36 *Madia sativa* compositae, a member of the Aster family.
37 Perhaps the term "control" is too Euro-centric in this context. The manner in which the Indians approached the exploitation of nature might be better characterized as a kind of facilitative process, one designed to let the land do most of the heavy lifting.
38 See Dr. Leland Gilsen's website (http://www.oregon-archaeology.com/theory/pyroculture/) for a thorough discussion of this technology as well as others employed by the Indians of the Willamette Valley.

Few things are more intrinsically human than the control and use of fire. Chimps and other animals use tools, at least very primitive versions of them, in much the same way we do; most animals, even many of the so-called lower order ones, communicate in one manner or another; and some animals even capitalize on the impact that fire might have on an area, much as proto-human populations may have. But I can't think of any other creature that controls and re-deploys fire. Humans have been doing this all around the planet for at least 200,000 years. Few other technological advances have had such a broad and profound impact on the development of human culture.

A holistic approach to the study of fire use and its impact on the social and cultural development of human populations in the Northwest is a relatively new idea, and didn't catch on in earnest until the 1930s when a geography professor named Carl Sauer and his students at Berkley came up with the idea of "fire economies."[39] The practice of using fire as part of the food quest was well understood where foraging and hunting were concerned, but Sauer's insight focused on the resulting alteration of landscapes and the long term effects of such action. In his view, much of the vegetation in pre-settlement America—the prairies of the Great Plains and the forests of the East Coast in particular—had been shaped by the use of fire as a tool in the food gathering process.

This "shaping" wasn't considered a premeditated act in Sauer's day. Rather, it was thought to be merely a providential side effect. Crediting Native American populations, particularly pre-settlement or Paleo-Indian populations, with a sophisticated approach to land management practices was out of the question. Even (or maybe especially!) during the early twentieth century, too many social and technological biases existed for scholars to entertain the notion that Indians actually exercised conscious control over their lives and their environments, or that their societies were in almost every way as rich and complex as our own. Historically, these biases represent two highly divergent perspectives—one leading to uncritical idealizations, the other to institutionalized intolerance. Both views are represented in the phrase "noble savage" and both are ethnocentric perspectives that have left us, even today, with a diminished appreciation for the possible realities of pre-settlement life in America.[40]

But the Kalapuya practice of managing the productivity of the land through the controlled and sustained use of fire was decidedly intentional. For at least 3,500 years these Native Americans exercised the art and craft of "pyroculture" throughout the length and breadth of the Willamette Valley, including the Tualatin River watershed.[41]

39 Sauer, 1950
40 Krech III, 1999
41 Gilsen, 2007

Controlled burn and aftermath—watershed management, Atfalati style, in Cook Park, Tigard

Reflect for a moment on what it means to actually control fire, at any scale of conflagration, in an open and non-mechanized environment. Imagine that one breezeless morning, you and a handful of your closest kin pack up your gear and set off across a limitless savannah covered with head-high grasses. You reach a stopping place that everyone can agree on , and suddenly you are standing there, fire implements in hand, about to put a select portion of the savannah to the torch. Maybe this is your first time, and although you know how it's done, you've never before been responsible for ensuring that at the end of the day none of your kinfolk are dead and the land has been burned in just the right manner—scorched and cleared of all undesirable growth, yet everything else of value left intact. What kind of composure, knowledge base, technical know-how, and group organization would that take? I equate it to the deep knowing exhibited by ancient Polynesians who navigated their boats through thousands of miles of open ocean.

By the time the Atfalati settled in the Fanno Creek watershed, burning the land to manage food production had become one of the more prosaic aspects of the Kalapuyan year. Most areas along the floor of the Willamette Valley and its side valleys were so well maintained that they had become almost park-like. At certain times of the year, vast expanses of the savannah were covered with waves of blue camas; at other times with yellow blankets of daisy-like tar weed. The margins in the uplands, and even the forested areas in the higher elevations, were fire-managed, usually to control the movements of game animals.

The Atfalati lived in what appears to have been a relatively stable society for at least a few thousand years. On their watch, the Tualatin Valley became a veritable Eden. Then, one day strange people with beards came into the country and, soon after, the entire world began to die.

The Utmost Good Faith[42]

By the time Augustus Fanno staked his claim to a full section[43] of farmland on Fanno Creek in 1847, diseases brought to America by European explorer-traders had been ravaging the Kalapuya for more than 60 years. Smallpox and venereal disease were epidemic in the late 1700s, devastating populations all along the Columbia and deep into the Willamette Valley. By the early 1800s some populations had just begun to rebound when an even more devastating epidemic struck, killing thousands of Indians outright and destroying their cultural infrastructure in the process. The disease was probably malaria, and the Indians were living in an environment tailor-made for the worst kind of epidemic.

The Kalapuya were sedentary in the sense that they tended to settle in distinct areas and remain in them indefinitely. Their foraging afield was seasonal

42 Language of the Northwest Ordinance, 1787
43 640 acres or 1 square mile of land.

and rarely took them more than a few miles from their permanent encampments. These villages were invariably located near wetlands that provided year round water and other subsistence needs. One of their main food resources was the wapato, a plant that favors the same shallow wetlands that are haunted by mosquitoes. Their proximity to prime mosquito habitat and their relatively fixed and communal life style virtually guaranteed that once an infectious disease was introduced among the Kalapuya it would spread like wildfire.

By 1833 there may have been fewer than 600 Kalapuyan souls left in the entire Willamette Valley. The ranks of the Atfalati had been equally decimated and many villages had been wiped out completely. Survivors from outlying areas began concentrating in the former cultural center of the valley, the main village near Lake Wapato. This consolidated victims as well as survivors. The disease moved through the totally vulnerable populations at great speed, killing virtually everyone who contracted it. The few survivors went from being nestled in the bosoms of their families one day to being entirely on their own a few days later. They had been forced to helplessly witness the prolonged and horrible deaths of their loved ones at the hands of an invisible and mysterious killer. For most of the remaining population, the cultural and emotional shock would have been as devastating as the disease itself. It is probably for this reason alone that the earliest settlers to the northwestern portions of Oregon experienced little or no meaningful Indian resistance as they began to lay claim to the entire Tualatin Basin.

Between 1843 and 1845 thousands of emigrants poured into Oregon, many of them arriving at Oregon City and then spreading out into the surrounding countryside. Acting on their own, some of the first settlers in the Willamette Valley wrote a constitution that established—in their minds at least—a land claim process. Augustus Fanno followed that process when he filed the first such claim in Washington County and took possession of 640 acres in the heart of the Fanno Creek watershed. It would be another three years before the American Congress would pass the Oregon Donation Land Act, a law that in essence validated most previous homestead claims in the state and further detailed the homestead process itself. Before the law expired in 1855, more than 2.8 million acres of prime Oregon property had been ceded to private individuals, none of whom were Indians[44] and none of whom were required to spend a dime for the property rights.

It's easy to imagine the anguish and anxiety that the few remaining Atfalati and other Kalapuya must have felt during this terrible time—easy and troubling. Their personal and tribal losses were extraordinary, easily comparable to those experienced by the Old World during the Plague. Unfortunately, things

44 Berg, 2007

were going to get much worse, particularly for small bands such as the Atfalati. The many bands of Kalapuya were never a unified tribe, never a distinct and recognized political entity. They built their influence and control over the areas of their range through a loose-knit set of extended, inter-family relationships based as much on proximity and language as on blood lines. But this way of building a society did not fit the Euro-American concept of tribalism. Regardless of their claim to the land before disease and fiat deprived them of their infrastructure and property, the Atfalati would have no future rights as a distinct people, and even fewer as individual persons. For all intents and purposes they were now "unpersons."[45]

In 1856 the federal government decided to relocate all the Indians remaining in the Tualatin Valley to the Grand Ronde reservation. As there was no chief to negotiate with, government officials appointed one. The task fell on the shoulders of a respected elder, a man named Ki-A-kuts. Not much is known about Ki-A-kuts, or any of the other Atfalati/Kalapuya leaders for that matter; but we can infer from his reputed statements, and the events to follow, that he was first and foremost a realist. Rightly or wrongly, his people would be relocated, and neither he nor the few remaining Atfalati possessed the power to do anything about it. "The Americans will never leave us alone," said Ki-A-Kuts. "Let us not concern our hearts...we will take [Grand Ronde]... [We] will make it our own place."[46]

By 1857 all surviving Kalapuya, including the Atfalati, were on reservations, with the majority at Grand Ronde. With their departure from the watershed went a style of ecosystem management that had sustained a proud and strong people for millennia without putting a strain on the watershed. These practices left behind a diverse assortment of forests, prairies, wetlands and waterways, all of them fertile, clean, and poised, in the sudden absence of the Atfalati, to return to the wild. But the wild would have to wait. On Fanno Creek many changes were taking place that would end up reshaping the Lower Tualatin watershed almost as drastically as the Missoula Floods. And in the midst of these changes, in a log house near the banks of Fanno Creek, Augustus Fanno's second wife, Rebecca Denney, was giving birth to their third child.

45 Coined by George Orwell to describe characters in his book *1984*, this term originally referred to people who had been vaporized and any aspect of their history expunged. During the cold war the term was used both literally and metaphorically to describe the fates of dissidents and other political criminals in the old Soviet Union.
46 Leaville, (1998). Interestingly enough Ki-A-Kuts is not one of the signatories of the 1855 treaty.

Fanno Farmhouse, built in 1859 from lumber sawed by Thomas Denney

4—Living in Interesting Times

Leaving Home

Fanno Creek can turn into a time machine if you catch the atmospherics just right. February is a good month for that. It's typically one of the coldest and wettest months in the year. Most mornings the wetlands and nearby forests emerge slowly from a pale darkness heavily laden with cold fog. The noise from nearby streets is so diminished that it could almost be mistaken for a stream running heavy with recent rains. On mornings like this the muted gray textures of the lowlands are pregnant with the ambiguities of time. One of the best places to witness such mornings is tucked away in a pocket-swamp at the north end of Greenway Park, just a few hundred yards from where Fanno Creek passes beneath Hall Boulevard.

I visit this place often because the area around it speaks volumes about the past and the future of Fanno Creek. Just a hundred yards upslope Rebecca Fanno, second wife of the creek's namesake, fed her chickens 150 years ago. This is one of the first areas along the creek where European ideas about "progress" began to overtake nature. Today it is one of the first places in the Tualatin Basin where a programmatic reversal of that degradation process is beginning to make headway.

Judging from old aerial photos,[47] something like this tiny area of swamp has been here for a long time. I'd guess that it's a remnant of the larger swamp that extended up and down the length of the middle stretches of the creek's floodplains prior to their conversion to farmland beginning in 1847. Seen from above, the area is shaped like a tadpole with its tail pointed due north and its mouth shoved up against the main stem of the creek. Most of the tail end is an overgrown ditch lying at the end of the drain pipe coming from a nearby grocery store parking lot.

The relatively open marsh runs on from the pipe for a couple hundred feet before it abruptly transitions from a mix of grasses and reeds to a dense thicket of willow, dogwood, hardhack and the like. This part of the swamp is so densely packed with brush that for most of the year it's impossible to see into the interior. But in the winter, when all the deciduous plants have lost their leaves, you can just make out a small wetland where a few mallards or maybe a solitary egret or blue heron can often be spotted working for a living. The confluence of the swamp's outlet and Fanno Creek lies in a flat, muddy area that floods at the drop of a hat.

Fanno Creek makes a series of particularly lovely meanders into and out of this marshy area. These meanders are tight and the creek moves them around

47 Corps of Engineers, 1969

constantly, so much so that an oxbow created in 2007 had turned into a fully surrounded island a year later. On the downstream end of this stretch beaver sometimes rebuild a good-sized dam that they've used on and off for several years. When the dam is intact and the creek is running high, the stream overtops its banks and turns the marsh into a shallow pond.

Technically this kind of wetlands area is called an emergent marsh.[48] It already teems with a wide variety of heron fodder—small fish, rodents, frogs, salamanders, and crayfish, to name just a few. Maybe someday the bird boxes back in the swamp will attract a wood duck or two. The area lies immediately adjacent to a couple of the most heavily used pathways in the park, but a substantial buffer of herbaceous and woody plants screens it from most of the nearby pathway. I caught site of a heron hanging around in there one evening, but it was getting too dark to photograph. I decided to come back the next morning and try to take a photo of him having his breakfast.

That morning the good news was that it wasn't raining. The bad news was that the fog was so thick I could barely see my hand in front of my face. I stepped off the path and worked my way as quietly as possible through the first few yards before getting down on my hands and knees for the final push to the creek. I'd been creek crawling for well over a year by then and had learned to gear up for bad weather excursions. I had on several layers of warm clothing, including good thermal underwear. I'd made a point of putting on rain trousers when I got out of the truck and wore insulated, waterproof gloves. Still, as my knees and palms began sinking into the soft mud the cold radiated up my arms and across my back. In less than ten minutes I could no longer feel the palms of my hands or my knee caps.

The deep blanket of fog had muted the sound of my footsteps on the pathway and I made an extra effort to move through the underbrush as quietly as possible. I took my time over the last few feet, and when I finally reached the creek I stretched out on my belly for a few minutes, listening and catching my breath before raising my head enough to look around. I didn't see the heron at first. Then he moved and I was startled by how near he was. His plumage was so close to the color of the foggy background that I had gotten within twenty yards before spotting him. I froze, waiting for him to focus on something other than the thin curtain of dead reed canary grass that separated us. When he shifted his gaze back to the ground near his feet, I slowly propped myself up on an elbow and began examining the scene.

There are few things more atavistic than the profile of a great blue heron at work, and while it is a common enough sight around here, it still captivates me. I watched him work for a long time—which is to say I watched him do noth-

48 Cowardian et al, 2008

ing for what seemed like an eternity. Then he took a couple of hyper-deliberate steps in my general direction and peered intently into some space directly in front of him. I must have blinked, because I never saw him strike; but suddenly he was choking down some unidentifiable gray thing that went swiftly to its demise with small appendages wiggling like mad all the while. In comic fashion the heron shook his head, and then bobbed his long neck up and down several times as if to clear it of some unwelcome obstruction. I could almost hear him say "yum."

I was hungry too, I suddenly realized. A tendril of wood smoke from a nearby but invisible fireplace floated by, followed seconds later by the distinct aroma of bacon. I let the comforting zephyr carry my thoughts away from the heron, back to the old Fanno Farmhouse 200 yards east and 150 years back in time. Which of the Fannos built the fire in the morning, I wondered, Eugene or his dad? What kind of kindling did they prefer? What type of wood did they like for the main fire, and what kind of a cook was Augustus? How often did they have pancakes? What about bacon? Did hogs wallow in the creek's mud not far from where I was stretched out on the soggy ground? Did the Fannos bring chickens with them, or did they buy them from a neighbor? Did they break bread with the Indians who lived just a ways upstream, or was the relationship confined to commerce? Most of all, how had young Eugene held up during those first few months along the banks of Fanno Creek? He would have been five years old, a mere child even by the standards of the day.

Thinking about Eugene took me back to my own childhood and for a few minutes I reflected on parallels and contrasts. I was just seven years old when my mother moved me and her broken heart into a remote part of the Ozarks to more or less hide out for a couple years. "Jessica James," she once laughingly— but bitterly—called herself. She was a divorcee rather than a widow, an identity which in those days not only robbed her of a husband but deprived her of the right to grieve even privately.

Home for those two years was a 12 by 24-foot pine shack with a tar-paper roof. There was no indoor plumbing and no electricity. Our water came from a spring that bubbled out of the mouth of a limestone cave 100 yards away from the shack. The place had one window, and any other interior lighting came from candles or a coal-oil lamp when we could afford to lay in some fuel. Heat came from a wood-burning cook-stove. There was no insulation so in the winters it was always chilly, no matter how much we fed the fire. In the muggy summers we stayed outside and in the shade until nightfall and the mosquitos drove us back inside. The closest of our few neighbors lived almost a mile away, and Nor-fork, the closest town, was a journey of more than eight miles over a rough and rarely traveled road. We had no car, and after the first winter no horses, so

"Shank's mare" was our primary mode of transportation. To make long trips we would stand by the side of the gravel road and hitch a ride with the first vehicle to chance by; wagon or car, they would always stop to pick us up.

We had no croplands, just a small garden with some corn, squash and beans. Nor did we have any livestock, not even a dog.[49] There were chores to be taken care of, to be sure—hauling water, cutting wood, tending the garden, clearing brush, washing dishes and clothes—and I was required to do my share of them. But my daily workload paled in comparison to the one that Eugene Fanno almost certainly shouldered. Demands made on children in the mid-nineteenth century were high, particularly regarding their contribution to the workforce. For children in pioneer families like the Fanno's, expectations were significantly higher. Augustus could count on his neighbors for help with some of the more difficult tasks, and he could hire a few Indians to help out as long as his meager funds permitted. But most of the time it was up to him and the little boy to get the work done. I'll bet Eugene was sick to death of weeding and hauling and chopping by the time he was seven. I know I was.

The heron's deep, croaking call broke through my reverie. He flew over my flattened body and headed for fresh hunting grounds further downstream. The fog was lifting. A slight breeze from the north had driven away the smell of bacon. It was time to move on. I rose stiffly, hobbled back to the path and headed for home. The first thing I was going to do when I got there was whip up a breakfast of bacon and flapjacks.

Augustus Fanno and His Times [50]

Augustus Fanno was born in Cumberland, Maine, just up the Atlantic coast from the other Portland. The year was 1804, a leap year and a momentous one at that. In England a man named Trevithick made the first locomotive-powered railway trip around his iron works on wooden rails; Napoleon became the Emperor of France and in the bargain got rid of a huge headache by formally transferring ownership of the Louisiana Purchase to the United States. Even before the ink was dry on that contract, a small party of 31 men,[51] along with a woman and her infant son, left a Mandan village and set off to change American history forever. Throughout his long life of 80 years Augustus lived in extremely interesting times.

By age 20 he had put to sea in the Merchant Marine. The service wasn't much older than Fanno, but was rapidly growing into one of the main components of the American economy. Joining the Merchant Marines was a logical and

---

49 The chief reason we had no livestock was that we couldn't afford to feed them during the winter months. There was barely money enough to feed even the two of us. And while I don't recall ever going hungry, my mom's tone invariably got a little grim whenever she reminisced in later years over the experience.
50 MacWilliam & Mapes (1984), Boag (1992), Hines (1893)
51 The Corps of Discovery

potentially profitable decision for a young man growing up along the eastern seaboard. Unfortunately, his career was cut short when a bout with yellow fever forced him ashore in New Orleans. Augustus was educated and resourceful, and while he was still convalescing he began teaching for a living. This career move was also cut short by yellow fever, but this time it was his students who came down with the disease. He moved on, stopping first in Mississippi for a few years before finally settling in or near Harrisonville in Van Buren County (now Cass County), Missouri, around 1830. By then Augustus was an accomplished and self-sufficient man of 26. At some point he met a young woman named Martha Ferguson and by 1833 they were married. They began to work a farm.

The fertile farmlands of Cass County were over 200 miles due west of St. Louis and still very much a part of the American frontier. Van Buren County, where the Fannos lived, wasn't formally organized until 1835 and Harrisonville, the county seat, didn't exist until 1837. The land that Augustus and Martha farmed had belonged to Indians less than thirty years earlier. Even in the mid to late 1830s hostilities continued to flare up in nearby areas of Kansas and Iowa. But the land was good farmland and the young couple continued to work it with apparent success for over a dozen years.

It isn't clear why the Fannos decided to leave Missouri for Oregon in 1847. Perhaps the production capacity of their land had begun to fade. Or maybe they got caught up in the fever of the Westward Expansion, as so many other Americans did during the period. The prospect of large tracts of high-quality land, free for the taking, inspired many others to jump at the chance of getting onto the Oregon Trail; why not Augustus? Or maybe he was just restless. He had been a seafaring man, so perhaps the idea of a new adventure appealed to him. The kind of freedom that a life at sea brings with it is not something easily forgotten, even by a man nearing midlife.

Whatever the stimulus, it was strong enough to propel the Fannos from the relative safety of western Missouri and onto a 2000-mile trek that would bring them to Oregon City six months later. By that time their first child, Eugene, was five years old and Martha was three months pregnant.

The Oregon Trail was well established, even heavily used, by the time the Fannos headed for Oregon; but it would have been a hard journey, nonetheless. Setting off for the Oregon Territory with a pregnant wife was not uncommon at the time and many children were born along the way. Still, the risks were legion and well-known. The death rate along the Oregon Trail was steep, maybe one in ten. Accidental injury, most frequently involving firearms, and diseases like cholera and dysentery were the big killers; but infant mortality and death by childbirth were common as well.

If either of the Fannos kept a journal or diary it never survived, so all that's known for sure is that they made it safely to Oregon City—the terminus of the trail—and a short time later went on to Linn City,[52] about three miles further west. The town lay along the favored route into the Tualatin Basin and was the last established community east of Forest Grove, 30 miles to the west-northwest. Most of the land in that immediate area had already been claimed by the time the Fannos arrived. It's possible that the family found lodgings in the town, or perhaps they pitched camp nearby. But they had not been in Linn City very long before a great tragedy overtook them. Martha died in childbirth, along with her baby.

When Augustus and Eugene stepped away from Martha's graveside they surely did so with heavy hearts. But despite their grief, they had much to do and very little time in which to do it. Competition for the remaining acreages in the Tualatin Basin was strong. More than 1,500 people had set off on the Oregon Trail in 1846, many of them leaving Missouri at the same time the Fannos had, and most of them had one thing on their minds: staking a claim to some of the finest farmland on the continent. Mourning would have to wait.

In those days a well-worn trail led out of Linn City in the direction of Forest Grove. It skirted the southern flanks of Cook's Butte, then turned north, passing through the gap between Mount Sylvania and Bull Mountain before veering to the northwest along the margins of the Fanno Creek floodplain. About ten miles from Linn City—a short-day's ride with a wagon full of gear and a few head of livestock—the trail crossed Fanno Creek, then headed north along the eastern flanks of Cooper Mountain. Something about this area must have appealed to Augustus because not long after his wife's death he laid claim to a full section of it—640 acres. More than half the property had good potential as farmland. It was low-lying, level, and almost certainly still displayed many of the hallmarks of a white oak savannah. The rest of the homestead tended towards timbered uplands. Just as the Atfalati had done before the arrival of the Euro-Americans, Fanno would be able to draw most of his essential materials and food-stocks directly from his land for years to come.

It's possible that Fanno built his first cabin not far from *Chachiamahiuk,* one of the known Atfalati villages identified by Gatschet.[53] A possible artifact from that time is located at the far-northeast corner of Fanno's original homestead—a remnant white oak savannah where camas still blooms from time to time.[54] A small band of Indians was encamped near this area when Augustus and Eugene arrived. For a while these Indians would be the Fanno's nearest neighbors.

---

52 Linn City was destroyed by flood in 1861. A new town, West Linn was built near the site.
53 Albert Samuel Gatschet (1832–1907) was a linguist and early ethnologist who studied a number of Indian cultures, including the Atfalati.
54 Camille Park.

Owning Oregon

In 1843 Britain and the United States were in the midst of the tension-filled process of determining how to divvy up the lands west of the Rockies. Accordingly, ownership of the Pacific Northwest was still an open question. For almost a century the British had exercised considerable control over the area through the operations of the Hudson Bay Company. But as more and more Americans arrived, the balance of power began to shift. These early arrivals chaffed under the company's Empire style of governance and eventually decided to set up a provisional government of their own. The seeds of self-governance were sown in 1841, when a prominent settler named Ewing Young died without having made a will. About 500 white settlers were living in the area then, and Young had had business dealings with a great number of them. Debtors and creditors met at Champoeg, just across the Willamette River from Young's ranch, and worked out an agreement for the disposal of his property.

More public meetings were held over the next few years, including the so-called "Wolf Meetings,"[55] which convened to discuss the problem of predators—wolves, bears and cougars—that were preying on livestock. A bounty system was proposed which would require the financial support of the larger community. Debate over the manner in which such funds would be collected and administered served as the fulcrum for moving the dialogue towards the establishment of a local government.[56] The Oregon Provisional Government emerged from these discussions and a comprehensive body of law soon followed. Collectively, these laws were known as The Organic Act; among them were statutes related to the ownership and taxing of land.[57]

In 1846 the United States and Great Britain signed the Oregon Treaty, which established the international boundary line along the 49th parallel. Two years later the Oregon Territory was established, and a year after that the first territorial governor arrived. The Provisional Government was promptly disbanded and the Organic Act repealed. Much about the homesteading process in Oregon would change under a new statute, including the manner in which property lines could be established and the number of acres that could be claimed. Called the Donation Land Claim Act (DLCA), the new law stipulated that from 1850 through 1853 a man could claim 320 acres for himself and the same amount for his wife, if he had one. But in 1854 that amount would be reduced to 160 acres. The law further stipulated that no one could claim more than a single donation of land in the territory. In this way the DLCA significantly limited land acquisition possibilities for future settlers. Fortunately for those who had settled their

55 Oregon Historical Society
56 Oregon History Project
57 When Fanno filed his claim he did so under the auspices of this act.

Augustus and Rebecca—on display during a Fanno family reunion held at the old farmhouse in 2009

lands under the Organic Act, the new law was written in a way that protected existing claims.

Fanno had filed his original claim to a full section of land on September, 22, 1847, shortly after the family's arrival in Linn City. When he re-filed with the new Oregon City Land Office in 1850 his claim was the first for land located in Washington County to be recorded under the DLCA, and only the 12th recorded overall. Why he enjoyed this kind of primacy isn't quite clear. Many other people were working land in the Tualatin Basin and the Willamette Valley well before Fanno arrived on the scene. Perhaps he simply showed up at the records office earlier than the rest. Or perhaps, even as early as 1849, he had become a well-known and important figure in the region—and by extension in the state. Judging from events that soon followed, it's likely that he had already established himself as a key player in the economic and political growth of the county and the region.

The Fanno Legacy

Eugene celebrated his sixth birthday on December 10, 1847. By then he and his dad were living in a hastily built log cabin not far from where the Fanno Farmhouse stands today. There was a great deal to do and very little time and help for doing it. There was wood to be chopped, stock to be tended, land to be cleared, water to be hauled, clothes to be mended, fields to be tilled, seed to be planted; the list goes on and on. Labor was hard to come by during this period of the Tualatin Basin's development, and neighbors didn't start arriving in force until at least a year after Fanno began working his claim.

Things began looking up a bit in 1849, however. Augustus had become acquainted with the Denneys, a pioneer family from Indiana that had arrived in the area in early October. The Denney contingent included three brothers, Thomas, Robert and Aaron; their sisters Rebecca and Elizabeth; Thomas's wife Barilla; and their cousins, Felix, John and James. Thomas, a sawyer, was looking for a place to set up a saw mill. He would need plenty of running water to operate his saw and Fanno knew exactly where he could find it. Before the year was out Thomas had laid claim to a full section of land adjacent to the Fanno's north-northeast property line. A sizeable portion of this land lay inside Fanno Creek's average annual floodplain, meaning that it generally flooded at least once in any given year. The water, properly channeled and dammed, would be a blessing for the sawyer and his family. By late 1850 the mill was up and running and Thomas began supplying milled lumber for many of the other homesteaders in the Tualatin Basin.

Thomas Denney had a sister named Rebecca. She was a spinster, age 31, and at some point she caught Augustus's eye. They tied the knot on April 17, 1851 and soon began to build a family of their own. Over the next ten years they had six children, of whom four lived to adulthood.

The tempo of life on Fanno Creek picked up considerably after the arrival of the Denneys and the subsequent Fanno-Denney marital alliance. To the north the fledgling community of Beaver Dam[58] was beginning to be a political and economic force in the region. To the south and east a continuing influx of new arrivals was rapidly gobbling up the few remaining parcels of free land in the Tualatin Basin. Even as the pace of settlement increased, so too did the complexities of governance for the territory. Each new group of settlers brought with them their well-established political and social viewpoints. By the mid-1850's the territory was as politically polarized as the rest of the nation.

In 1853 the Washington Territory was split off from the original Oregon Territory. This signaled that Oregon would almost certainly be entering the Union as a state in its own right before many more years passed. Like his closest neighbors and other nearby settlers in the Beaver Dam area, Fanno was deeply opposed to slavery; he was determined to do everything he could to ensure that Oregon entered the Union as a free state. He became politically active and in 1856 even ran for a council seat in the local precinct elections. Perhaps the most important aspect of Fanno's politics is that he not only worked for the admittance of Oregon as a free state, but strove for the right of free blacks to enter. In the end he and like-minded men were only half successful. In 1847 the men of the Territory voted on the issue of statehood and the ratification of the constitution. The vote for statehood was 7,195 for; 3,215 against. The vote against slavery was even more emphatic: 7,727 to 2,645 against. But while folks were ready to enter the Union and determined to keep slavery out of the state, they were less interested in extending the rights of citizenship to people of color. The vote against allowing free blacks to enter the state was 8,640 to 1,081. Oregon entered the Union as a free, but intolerant state on February 14, 1859.

Fanno's reaction to this split in the vote is unknown. He remained active in local politics for a time, but as the years progressed he began to focus more on farming than politics. He had become interested in breeding an onion that would be more highly resistant to the Pacific Northwest's relatively cool and damp weather, a goal he accomplished after twenty years of experimentation. In the process he succeeded in becoming the largest producer of onions in the entire state of Oregon.

Not far from one of the busiest retail areas in northwestern Oregon lies the Crescent Grove cemetery. Established in 1852, this is the oldest maintained cemetery in the Portland metropolitan area. Augustus is buried there. I stopped by for my first visit in 2009. It was a typical mid-November afternoon: dark,

58 Predecessor of today's Beaverton.

rainy and cold. A sharp wind fussed with my rain jacket. I was struck by the fact that this could easily have been the same kind of weather that Augustus and his little boy had stood in more than 160 years earlier, in that graveyard back in Linn City. How long did they stand bareheaded beside Martha's grave before they finally turned to go? I took off my hat and stood for a while myself, ignoring the ice-cold rain running down the back of my neck. I'd brought along a small bouquet. Nothing fancy, just a few blue irises with a dozen or so green onions bundled around their stems. I placed it on the simple rectangular granite stone that marks Fanno's final resting place and headed back to the truck.

We talk a lot about the pace of change these days, sometimes shaking our heads and marveling out loud at how hard it is to keep up with it all. But in the 80 years between 1804 and 1884 an entire continent and everyone on it was changed in ways we still don't fully comprehend. Fanno had not only been swept up in those changes, he had fashioned a number of them himself. When I reflect on his accomplishments and his times the very first word that springs to mind is "citizen." He was, among other things, the kind of man who exercised his rights primarily so that he might better do his duty.

Fanno Creek, between Paul's place (top) and the problem-plagued BES sewage pumping station

5—The Urban Stream Syndrome[59]

The Poo Problem

My friend Paul and I stood on the patio in his back yard. It was raining, not enough to drive us back inside, but enough to make us hurry through our discussion. Just past the edge of the patio and at the bottom of a nearly vertical embankment, the muddy, frothy waters of Fanno Creek went rushing by. A similar embankment rose from the other side of the creek, this one topped by a black chain-link fence overplanted with an odd assortment of deciduous saplings and evergreen shrubs. Several evenly spaced, rangy young conifers made a picket just behind the fence. These acted as a partial screen for a large red-brick building lying deeper into the property. A pair of large metal boxes stood at the south end of the building. They were painted bright orange.

"Those are the pumps," said Paul. Then he gestured toward a pile of gray rocks that took up most of the area between the pumps and the fence. "That pile of rocks between the building and the fence lies on top of the hole I told you about. That's where the sewage is supposed to go when the pumps fail. And when that baby fills up, guess where the extra sewage is supposed to go after that? Over the embankment and right into the creek! They have to be out of their minds!"

"They" was Portland's Bureau of Environmental Services (BES) and the hole was just the most recent episode of a sewage nightmare that has plagued this portion of Fanno Creek for decades. "I've seen enough," I said, and we went back inside.

"What do you think?" Paul asked as we drank our coffee. I hardly knew where to begin and had more questions than observations.

"So, that complex was there when you moved in, right?"

He nodded and began describing the chain of events that led to the excavation of the hole and the installation of the giant pumps. A few years back, he and his wife had embarked upon a major remodel. They knocked out several walls to open up the relatively low-ceilinged space, reworked and re-equipped the kitchen, and put in new flooring throughout most of the house. Then they installed a row of floor-to-ceiling, energy efficient sliding windows that opened up most of the interior and visually extended it onto a spacious patio. Just past the edge of the patio lay the creek.

The project had been costly, but in the end was well worth the expense. The interior looks like it just stepped out of an architectural magazine. Paul is a realtor, a savvy one. He knew they might be pushing against the equity ceiling for their home a little, but felt they had been able to keep the total investment

59 Walsh et al (2005)

well inside any foreseeable market fluctuations. But while he had been able to anticipate a downhill movement in the housing market, he had never anticipated the ghastly business that would one day take place directly outside his back door.

When Paul and his wife purchased their home they felt they were getting a good deal. They had done the homework that any responsible couple should do. They knew the house lay on the margins of a floodplain—proximity to the creek had been a plus in their eyes. They believed the likelihood of a serious flood reaching the home was extremely remote. In any event, they could get affordable flood insurance that would cover such a contingency. And as for the big red-brick building on the adjacent property...well, it wasn't all that bad looking. Besides, the trees and shrubs BES had planted on the property would eventually block the view, except in the deepest part of the winter.

What they didn't know about the building when they bought the house was that there were powerful pumps inside the shed that were not actually working at the time. When the machinery finally came back online shortly after they moved in, Paul and his wife experienced a serious shock. The noise was more than a simple annoyance, even when all their doors and windows were shut. From time to time the house actually vibrated from the action of the pumps. When summer came their anger and anxiety mounted. Because of the noise their lovely patio remained unused; their windows and French doors remained unopened. Then, just when they thought they couldn't take it anymore, the pumps suddenly went silent.

A short while later a notice from BES appeared in their mailbox, advising them of developments at the pump station that were almost surely going to worsen the situation. The pump station was experiencing difficulties and would need to be expanded, perhaps to as much as double its existing size.

It's Gravity, Stupid

Fanno Creek and all but a few of its major tributaries get their headwaters off hilltops and slopes within the City of Portland's jurisdiction. Miles of sewer pipes servicing multiple Portland neighborhoods run through these drainage ways. For decades, handling the sewage from these neighborhoods has proved to be a difficult, expensive and ultimately embarrassing task for the BES. At one time the organization operated five pressure sewers and pump stations designed to move the sewage out of the Fanno Creek watershed and into Portland treatment plants east of the Tualatin Hills ridgeline. After struggling for years with inadequate pumping equipment on these multiple sites BES decided to build a high-capacity pumping station at one of the lowest points in the area. This turned out to be the large lot directly across Fanno Creek from Paul's back yard.

From the very beginning there were multiple problems with this site, not the least of which was that it located the terminus for collection of the Portland effluent on Washington County property. After a bit of negotiation the county obligingly struck the necessary leasing deal with Portland. The project began with the construction of a pair of high-pressure sewage lines that would need to push the waste from the pump station to a BES collection point 250 feet higher and three miles away in the Tualatin Hills. From there the effluent flow could be managed using a system driven primarily by gravity.

The older sections of Portland's sewage system were designed to manage both sewage and surface water runoff. As a result, the collection point itself had to be big enough to hold the sudden surge in both sewage and rainwater that occurred during heavy rains in the uplands areas of the West Slope. Every significant rain event would bring hundreds of thousands of gallons of fluid into the holding facility—the big red-brick building behind Paul's home. From there the massive pumps inside the building would push the accumulation uphill and into Portland's jurisdiction.

One afternoon in February of 2000, as work on the 18-million-dollar project was nearing completion, construction personnel tested the pipe. It failed, spectacularly so. Seals at various spots along the line blew out; in one spot a half mile away the force blew steel plates covering sewer construction high into the air. According to one witness, it sounded as if a plane had crashed in the neighborhood. The saga of the Fanno Creek Pump Station had begun.[60]

Repairs were made and the pump station was brought back online. But major failures continued to plague the project. In 2002 sewage spewed out through broken pipes and onto a newly completed section of the Fanno Creek trail running through Portland's Garden Home neighborhood. A 2005 failure sent over 500,000 gallons of untreated sewage into Fanno Creek. The spills continue to occur at frequent intervals. One in 2008 sent 1,800 gallons into the creek, and one in 2011 sent an additional 150 gallons into the creek. This one was a little bit of a surprise to everyone because the station had been offline since 2008. As it turns out, sewage somehow still finds its way to the area and has to be collected, then periodically sent through a temporary pipe leading to a manhole connected to the Clean Water Services system.

Because of these setbacks the BES finds itself in a difficult situation. As the agency is quick to point out, it scarcely matters who or what is to blame for past failures of the system; doing nothing is simply not an option. For the short term a "fix" of sorts is in place. Currently the bulk of the Garden Home outflow is pumped into the Clean Water Services system and processed at the Durham plant. This will handle most of the problem during the dry season and even into

60 Van Der Voo (2008)

the time of year when precipitation is moderate. Unfortunately, that encompasses no more than four to six months of the year, so a second fix is in place for the periods when peak rains lead to capacity issues on the BES/CWS line. Hence the catchment in the lot behind Paul's house.

A few days later Paul called me again. "Come over here if you can. The BES is giving us a tour of the area today and you are not going to believe your eyes. They're also going to show us the plans they have for a second station."

I rushed over in time to join Paul, his wife, and the bureau's spokesperson for the project, an amiable young man named Stephen. As a friend of mine put it, Stephen has "one of the shittiest jobs in the sewer business." We entered the property through a gate on the side furthest from Paul's house, then walked around to where the pumps squatted silently on their concrete foundations. Up close and personal they and the building were even more massive than I had realized. Stephen had brought along a couple of large drawings and soon was going over these with Paul. Paul's wife and I were drawn further into the property by an amazing sight. In the small space between the pump station and the black chain-link fence, a hole twenty or thirty feet in diameter had been dug into the ground, then filled to overflowing with large gray boulders. A pair of pipes led from the pump station to two large concrete blocks nestled into the giant gravel. Plenums, I figured, for the effluent that would issue from the pump station's inner well when rain events exceeded the basic capacity of the system. That much made sense to me, but when Stephen and Paul joined us I asked how the thing worked, just to be sure.

Stephen explained that this rock well served as a stilling basin. Its primary purpose was to reduce the energy of the flow enough to minimize erosion of the embankment between the point of overflow and the creek. It was deep and would handle a large amount of outflow for a time. But ultimately it would overflow; when it did, the effluent, now relieved of some solid materials and highly diluted with stormwater (but still raw sewage for all of that), would flow over the lower lip, then across the ground, where gravity would lead it down the embankment and into the creek.[61]

Before I could collect my wits and open my mouth, Stephen said, "Yes, I know. It's a lousy solution, but there just isn't anything else we can do.[62] Our best hope is that for the next two years the rains will be mostly moderate. In the meantime we are planning on moving ahead with expanding the facility and building a more reliable piping system. That's why I brought these plans along, so you can see what we'll be doing here to fix this problem once and for all."

61 "It's important to note that this relief system only gets used in the event that the excess flow (that currently diverts to CWS) becomes more than CWS's can handle." Sykes, personal communication 2/15/2012.
62 Technical Memorandum BES (2008)

I went through the motions of looking at the drawings, pretending to be interested and impressed. But the truth is I was in shock and remained that way until much later in the day. I could not erase from my mind the image of thousands of gallons of sewer water running down the embankment and into the creek. Surely there had to be better answer, such as giving all the stuff to cws to handle. They'd need to add capacity in order to stay current with long term projections, and there might be some pipe issues to be resolved, but why wouldn't that work?

I wasn't convinced that building an additional 11,000 square feet of facility and ramping up the pumping capacity would prove any more expensive than increasing cws's infrastructure and capacities needed to handle the additional load. I also wasn't convinced that it would put a stop to sewage overflows in the area. These concerns turned out to be two of the main themes developed at a neighborhood meeting I attended a week or two later. A group of Paul's neighbors, including several whose properties would be significantly impacted by the project, had gathered to develop support against the proposed plan. There were at least thirty people in the crowd and most of them were angry.

"It's gravity, stupid! Shit flows downhill and everybody knows that but those freakin' bureaucrats at BES." These words from a red-faced, older gentleman standing near the back of the crowd pretty much summed up the prevailing attitude. Up toward the front people were milling around, waiting for someone to get the meeting underway, but no one seemed to be in charge. Then, just when it looked as though the meeting would fall apart, a youngish-looking woman stepped to the front and began to speak. Her voice was a bit high pitched and didn't project particularly well. She was stepping into the middle of a very frustrated crowd that was noisy and distracted and spoiling for a fight. But while she didn't have Gandhi's vocal talents, she had his kind of grit. She also had help from several of her neighbors, and soon was able to get the group to focus on some necessary objectives. In less than half an hour they were able to organize into a coherent body, articulate a basic action plan and establish a simple communications process. A number of the individuals involved were professional people, I reminded myself, folks who held management positions in medium-to-large firms. They knew how to build teams, make agendas, and execute plans. I got the impression that they would almost certainly turn out to be a handful for the BES to manage.[63]

When the meeting began to break up I introduced myself to the organizer. Her name was Jennifer and one corner of the property she and her husband owned went right down to the creek. We discussed the situation for a moment

---

63 In point of fact they managed to bring the project to a standstill and ultimately forced the BES to begin looking for an alternate site.

and then I asked if I could come by sometime in the next few days and cross over her property so that I could walk the undeveloped area between her yard and the pump station. She was eager for me to see the area, and also her home. "You may not know this, but the area in which we live is very important, architecturally. Many of the homes, including ours, are 'Rummers.' That's one of the reasons we bought there." The word drew a blank, but I later learned that a builder named Robert Rummer had built a large number of homes in the area, basing their construction on the earlier work of Joseph Eichler (1900–1974).[64]

Eichler had been a real estate man, not an architect, but he was progressive aesthetically and socially. He hired architects with lineages that included such greats as Frank Lloyd Wright and Mies van der Rohe. That's impressive enough in its own right, but Eichler also used non-discriminatory practices in an era and an industry where discrimination toward home buyers was an entrenched practice. A key characteristic of many of his homes is that they are designed to eliminate the structural barriers that typically keep a home and its environment separated. As a rule they are open, airy, full of light and tend to bring the feeling of the outdoors into the interior living spaces. Rummer was an admirer, and many of his homes accomplished the same objectives, including the one on the banks of Fanno Creek that Jennifer showed me through a few days later.

The tour helped me feel Jennifer's pain more acutely. We stood in the backyard and looked into the greenery that physically and visually separated the home from the pump station. "I can't bear the thought of this being gone," she said. She stood with her arms tightly folded across her chest and stared into the BES property. No quivering lip, no beginning of tears at the corners of the eyes, not the slightest hint of a cave in. But she was feeling it deeply, nonetheless. I could tell by the set of her jaw that Jennifer was not at all ready to resign the matter to fate. Fanno Creek could use a few more advocates like her, I decided.

I wiggled through a hole in the fence and began a slow walk over the area where the BES would almost certainly be building before much longer. While the neighbors might complain as vociferously as they wanted to, the agency owned the property and had all the necessary permits to operate there. Unless something in those permits could prevent expansion of the facilities, then it was pretty much a done deal, at least as far as I could foresee.

By the time I reached the middle of the property I was more convinced than ever that the small acreage was doomed. It was similar to most of the other so-called "green belts" that thread their ways through residences built on or in floodplains: ignored more than loved; functional as a screen but only borderline functional as habitat; neglected but not abused; mostly forgotten or overlooked. In several places neighbors had used the area as a dumping ground

64 Rummer Connection blog at http://site.rummernetwork.com/

for lawn clippings, dead potted plants, and even a very old and dry Christmas tree. But other than a rusty bike tire, there was no sign of litter. There were no pathways anywhere, either, not even a game trail.

On the way out I stopped and talked to Jennifer. We walked over to the little triangular section of her property giving direct access to the creek and looked upstream, along the embankment that would someday be covered in a viscous sheet of raw sewage. I could say little to cheer her up or set her mind at ease. As far as I could tell, there was nothing in the way of ecosystem assets that might be of use in any sort of negotiations, I told her, reminding her that I was merely a writer and photographer. Maybe someone else with more solid credentials could survey the area? They might see something I had overlooked. She asked who I might recommend and I told her that I would email her a list of organizations and individuals that might be interested in the situation.

"What do you really think?" she finally asked.

I hesitated, wanting to say something helpful, but painfully aware that I had no real credentials and more than that, no really useful information. "I think you have to get Washington County involved somehow, or Metro, or preferably both. You need to get your government to fight for you. You live in Washington County and this is really Portland's problem."

She was visibly frustrated by my advice. "We've been trying to, but they've told us we have to communicate with the BES and Portland. None of us can understand why that's the case, but we've all gotten the same run-around. Then, when we call Portland, we end up talking to the same guy. Stephen somebody. He's a nice man and obviously just telling us what he's told to say. None of us want to kill the messenger..." She turned and looked back into the greenery. "I just can't believe no one is going to do anything to stop all this."

If the creek could have spoken to us at that moment it might well have said the same thing.

Road to Ruin

A decade after Augustus Fanno first became smitten with Rebecca Jane Denney his farm and all the others along the banks of Fanno Creek resembled those back east during the same era. They were home to chickens, cattle, horses, rabbits, dogs, hogs and numerous cats. There were a growing number of outbuildings on the properties, including barns, smokehouses, chicken coops and privies. Row crops and pasturelands surrounded the stream on most of its lower reaches, many coming directly down to the edge of cleared banks. Around the houses, out in the freshly broken fields and along property lines, new species of plants were springing up. Most had been brought along intentionally, packaged carefully as seeds back in Missouri or Indiana, and carefully planted and tended upon arrival. Others arrived more providently by hitching rides on wagons, animals, clothing and packing materials. The long-term impact of domestic animals and plants on the creek and its watershed would be as profound as the impact of the settlers themselves.

The character and functionality of Fanno Creek began to change drastically, particularly along its main stem between Beaverton and its confluence with the Tualatin River. Most of the large timber growing in and around the margins of the floodplain was gone within a few years, cut down to increase the farmable acreage or for woodstoves and lumber. Where they could, the farmers also increased the effective acreage of their land by draining and filling wetlands. They straightened the creek's channel to make irrigation more efficient. For similar reasons, brush was cleared off the property all the way down to the water's edge. Berms or levees were erected along portions of the creeks that tended to flood most frequently.

Driven mostly by gold rushes in northern California and southern Oregon, Washington County's economy was very strong. Farming was still the principal industry, but each year the population in the Fanno Creek watershed increased significantly as new waves of emigrants poured into the state. The increase in numbers brought with it an increase in commercial and industrial capacity. Tanners, blacksmiths, wood workers and other skilled craftsmen began to arrive in force.

Roads, most of them built and maintained in the beginning at private expense, cut across the watershed. A plank toll road running east to west through a deep canyon in the Tualatin Hills connected the Tualatin Valley with the rapidly growing city of Portland. It was called Canyon Road, and a good portion of it ran through the upper reaches of the Fanno Creek watershed. The road made it possible for farmers and their produce and livestock to bypass the long trip down the Tualatin River to Oregon City. This helped secure Portland's position as the primary shipping center on the Willamette River. At the same time, the new road increased the flow of population into the Fanno Creek watershed, as well as the rest of the Tualatin Basin. The Fanno farm was located just a few miles south of this critical artery, and when it was finished the Fannos were able to cut the distance to market by more than half.

In those earliest days of settlement the creek provided a wide range of beneficial uses: water to drink, water for household chores, water for livestock, for crops, for irrigation, for power; and a place to fish and swim in the summer.[65] Because of this heavy use and the damage done by draining, filling, clearing and straightening the of its streambeds, the creek was beginning to fade. Still,

---

· 65 Some sections of it also could be easily navigated at certain times of the year and served as short transportation corridors.

it was relatively free of major pollutants, despite waste from domestic animals. For a couple of decades it was the floodplain, the uplands and the air that took the real beating from pollution. In the mid-1800s the ground was typically the place where people dumped waste products that wouldn't burn. Open trenches or outhouses were the repositories for bodily waste, while ditches or pits were used for trash and other waste manufactured by people going about their day to day business. But before the century was out Fanno Creek would be asked to handle the first wave of a load of pollutants that would prove to be more than it could recover from on its own.

The septic tank wasn't patented until late in the 1880s, and probably didn't make its way to the Pacific Northwest until a decade or two later at the earliest. However, the flush toilet in one form or another has been around for millennia.[66] It's unclear exactly when the first modern flush toilets began to appear in the Fanno Creek watershed. They were in Portland as early as 1864, so it is reasonable to assume that they began to be used in areas adjacent to the city sometime shortly thereafter. It's also unclear how widely used flush toilets were before the turn of the century. While the technology was simple enough, the toilets themselves would have remained a bit of a luxury until a sewage transport system could be developed. Early transport devices were crude, sometimes simply a V-shaped covered trough that ran out of residences above ground, then into the nearest swale or creek. But progress was inevitable; by the 1880s more sophisticated sewage systems consisting of buried pipes were a standard feature of the urban areas around the heart of the Fanno Creek watershed.

In Portland, the sewer system grew from a few miles in 1883 to well over a thousand miles just fifty years later. The effluent from this system included feces, urine, flushing water, stormwater and the gray water from kitchens and lavatories. It also included a wide range of industrial wastes from the heavy industries beginning to be widespread throughout the area. All of it went into the nearest stream, which, in the case of Portland's more metropolitan areas, was the Willamette River. But much of Portland's earliest growth took place along the main communications routes to the north, the south and the west. By the turn of the century Portland's rapid growth was spilling into the northeast and eastern reaches of Fanno Creek's extensive tributary network. Cut off from easy and economical access to the Willamette River, these residential areas simply used the nearest available tributaries for their sewage dumping grounds.

By the turn of the twentieth century the population of Portland had grown to just over 900,000 people, many of whom made the Tualatin Hills their home. At the same time, nearly 15,000 people were living in the Tualatin Basin. More were on the way, and many of the newcomers would settle in the eastern por-

66 1000 BCE according to Bindeshwar (1995).

tion of the Basin. The Fanno Creek watershed was rapidly becoming one of the more densely populated areas in the state. With the increased urbanization came a steadily increasing effluent bill. Sewage systems in the area were adding infrastructure as rapidly as possible, but the technology itself remained primitive at best. The streams on both sides of the Tualatin Hills ridgeline were increasingly at risk. Still, funding improvements to sewage systems remained a hard sell for decades to come. People might complain, particularly those closest to the increasingly filthy waterways, but political will was woefully lacking when it came to forking out money to do anything about the mess.

An example of the kind of political disconnect that existed throughout the region until well into the middle of the twentieth century can be glimpsed in the following excerpt from a short article recently written about the evolution of Portland's sewer system:[67]

> In the early 20th Century, public concerns about water pollution and public health increased. Tests in 1927 showed that the Willamette flowing through Portland was severely polluted. By the mid-1930s salmon fingerlings placed in the [Willamette] river died within 15 minutes.... Swimming was banned. Citizens took action. More than 4,000 schoolchildren held a rally outside City Hall *in November 1938* to demand cleanup of the river. Later that year, Oregon voters initiated and passed the Water Purification and Prevention of Pollution Bill. A newly established State Sanitary Authority began to enact waste water treatment requirement for both cities and industries. Portland responded by building the Columbia Boulevard Wastewater Treatment Plant and a new system of collection pipes and pump stations. *The plant opened in 1952* and began discharging treated wastewater into the Columbia River. [italics mine]

That regulations were passed and that the state and city took action are positive points, to be sure, and they created some of the initial framework needed to control the development of the state's lands. But by the time any effective remedy took place the water pollution issue was well over fifty years old. Things were a bit better over in the Tualatin Basin, at least for a while, but only because the population base was smaller and the area involved much larger. Still, in the eastern portion of the basin the bulk of Fanno Creek's upper watershed was experiencing exactly the same kind of treatment that streams east of the Tualatin Ridge had to endure during the same timeframe.

67 Portland Online.

Drano Creek

After World War I the pace of residential and commercial development in the watershed began to accelerate dramatically. Farmland and other undeveloped property began to vanish under waves of residential and commercial projects. The passage of the Water Purification and Prevention of Pollution Bill had led to the requirement for at least mechanical treatment of the raw sewage being pumped into the open streams. By the 1960s there were treatment plants operating from half a dozen places in the creek's watershed. Any treatment was better than none, but in the end these facilities were either too small, too poorly built or too poorly managed to do more than briefly slow down the rate of the creek's degradation.

By the late 1960s Fanno Creek was little more than an open sewer, particularly in the dry season, when effluent from the several[68] first-stage treatment plants along its banks were providing more gallons of waste fluids to the stream than the recharge from its aquifer would ordinarily produce. Winter rains could bring some partial relief by diluting the sludge and garbage collected over the summer, then moving it downstream and finally into the Tualatin River. However, many properties throughout the Fanno Creek Watershed were still on septic tanks, and if the rains were heavy enough the contents of these tanks and their attendant drain fields would simply add to the creek's miseries.

Sewage was not the only problem for the creek, however. Commercial and residential development was still occurring at a breakneck pace. Of the 32 square miles of surface area in the watershed, fully 20 percent had already disappeared under a blanket of solid concrete and much more would follow in the decades to come. A substantial portion of the land that remained free of roads, houses, malls, warehouses, parking lots, gas stations and schools was dedicated to farms and dairies. The surface areas of these more agrarian installations provided a little more permeability than concrete, but the stormwater runoff from their usually barren and compacted feed lots and well-grazed pastures was still considerable. It was also loaded with manure and other noxious animal byproducts.

As the amount of permeable land decreased, the behavior of streams in the watershed began to change in ways that worsened the pollution problem and the declining health of the creek. In stormy weather the creek and its tributaries became increasingly flashy, which exacerbated the in-stream erosion, adding even more sediments to the watershed's already badly polluted system of streams. To cap it all off the end of the Second World War had brought with it a phenomenal increase in the use of pesticides and other chemicals the likes

---

68 There were a total of 26 individual plants throughout the Tualatin Basin, according to CWS literature. TOPO maps for the period show six sites in the Fanno Creek watershed alone.

of which the natural world had never seen before. In retrospect, an astonishing level of carelessness and outright stupidity accompanied the unleashing of these toxins on the unsuspecting countryside. Most of the common "garden variety" insecticides of that era have been banned by now, or their use strictly regulated. However, even today we do not completely understand the full dimensions of the dark legacy left behind by the introduction of post-World War II chemicals into the environment.

View Master

Less than half a mile east of where Augustus and Eugene first camped along the banks of Fanno Creek lies Cascade Plaza, there's a small commercial complex of mostly retail stores standing today. From 1951 to 2001 the 52-acre site was home to the View Master plant.[69] The View Master was one of the most successful 3-D viewing devices ever made. Between 1939 and 2009 production of the viewer itself ran into the millions, the reels it used into the billions. The company changed hands several times, finally being bought by Tyco Toys, Inc. in 1989, which in turn merged with Mattel in 1997.

Until the late 1980s the cleaning process used on some of the machinery involved in production of the device and its reels employed the solvent TCE (trichloralethelene) to treat the accumulation of lubricants and other petrochemical substances on tools and machines. At the time the chemical was known to pose significant health risks to humans; it is now a known human carcinogen. For approximately 20 years it was View Master's practice to dump spent solutions directly onsite. This dumping took place legally and routinely at several places around the site. In 1970 the company began recycling the material and in 1980 they stopped using it altogether.

The manufacturing site included a well that used to supply drinking water for employees. In 1996 a routine inspection discovered that the water in this well was contaminated with TCE in concentrations 300 times higher than the federal drinking water standards. Other volatile organic compounds were discovered in the well at the same time. Original estimates placed the number of potentially exposed employees at 25,000, but further research over the intervening years has reduced that number to around 1,000. Many of these former employees continue to seek answers about long-term health issues that may be associated with their exposure at the plant, but definitive links between the chemical and the specific issues many of them contend with have been hard to establish, scientifically and legally.

---

69 There were actually three parcels of land that made up the View Master property, two of which made up the Cascade Plaza acreage and a third piece of land of about 30 acres that lay immediately to the west.

The Oregon Department of Environmental Quality (DEQ) completed its clean-up of the site in 1998, and in 2004 reported that amounts of TCE had reached acceptable levels. Shortly thereafter the construction of Cascade Plaza commenced. But while that portion of the old View Master site had been deemed safe, another section of the property was still under the scrutiny by the DEQ. About half of this area was part of a large, shallow lake that was separated from Fanno Creek by a small weir. The lake and its adjoining marshy areas are known as the Koll Wetlands and it is currently listed on the state's 303(d) list of impaired water bodies.[70] The Koll Wetlands teem with life, birds in particular, and at first glance you might not notice the small, rectangular structure sitting on the bank just above the high-water mark at the southwest corner of the lake, or even the large hose connecting it to the water. This relatively unimposing structure has been on this site since 1998 and is there to monitor water quality, particularly the levels of heavy metals present in the lake. These include chromium, copper, iron, lead, manganese, silver and zinc. To what degree the View Master operation contributed to this potentially poisonous legacy is impossible to say. But the dark-gray vault housing the DEQ equipment stands as an emblem of an era in which limited regulation and careless use of potentially toxic chemicals regularly poisoned Fanno Creek and everything that swam in it.

For Fanno Creek the situation finally came to a head in 1969, when the State imposed a temporary moratorium on development in all of Washington County. By then all of the major streams in the Tualatin Basin were in terrible shape, but Fanno Creek was still everyone's favorite poster child. The locals called it Drano Creek and for a substantial portion of its length it was a filthy, stinking, dangerous mess. On some days you could smell it well before you could see it.

The moratorium hit at a time when the entire region was experiencing a growth spurt. The specter of lost profits galvanized the business community into supporting strong civic action. By 1971 the citizens of Washington County had approved the establishment of a new utility that unified the 26 separate sewage treatment facilities then operating throughout the Tualatin Basin into a single organization. It was named the Unified Sewerage Agency and it was just getting underway when the Clean Water Act of 1972 was enacted. The EPA, which was charged with enforcement of the law, was just two years old. The times they were a-changing, or so it seemed.

70 See http://water.epa.gov/lawsregs/lawsguidance/cwa/tmdl/overview.cfm (EPA) for a more detailed overview of what 303(d) lists are and where they fit in the effort to meet a variety of water-quality issues.

Marlene's sandbag moat (top), and the home site after demolition for wetlands mitigation

6—The Hydrology of Hell

Eartha the Clown

Lola peeked at me from behind the shower curtain, uncertain for a moment, then waddled out onto the floor and headed toward a dark corner behind the commode. She was uneasy, but perhaps Marlene's presence was reassuring enough to keep her from actually hissing and baring her fangs at me. Instead, she simply continued giving me the hairy-eyeball as she made her way into the deeper shadows behind the porcelain pedestal.

"Why 'Lola,' ?" I asked. "That's a pretty sexy name for a possum."

Marlene immediately came to the creature's defense. "She's beautiful," she scolded, "and if you knew anything about them, you'd know that." She picked Lola up and stroked her for a moment before putting her back onto her blanket in the tub. "The name just seemed to fit at the time. I've learned that names like this help take away some of the fear people sometimes have right up front. I have had over a dozen show opossums with names like Blossom, Flower, Petal, Ozzie, Olivia, Rosie. My favorite was Blossom the Awesome Possum. She was truly awesome."

Marlene then proceeded to dazzle me with possum facts. Did I know that they are America's only marsupial, equivalent in many ways to Australia's kangaroo or koala; that they are actually quite clean, in spite of their reputation to the contrary; that they are less likely to carry rabies than any other wild mammal; and did I know that they eat all kinds of nasty things, like cockroaches and slugs? I looked around the bathroom for lingering signs of past meals and Marlene laughed.

"I feed her vegan dog food. She loves it."

From the bathroom we moved to one of the spare bedrooms that house her large collection of rescued parrots, love birds, and cockatoos. Dozens of beautiful birds chattered away in a wide variety of cages that Marlene has rummaged, bought, or received as donations over the years. We lingered for a moment to admire spectacular displays of different plumages, and I found myself wishing, as I have so many times in the past, for a place to keep a parrot. They are amazing animals but messy beyond belief.

"Nonsense," snorted Marlene when I shared this negative observation. "They are no worse than a two-year-old child. Believe me, I know."

An image of my grandson, Jake, came to mind. He had recently turned two and I reflected on the kind of messes he regularly made with things like Cheerios, green beans, ice cream and the like. I rested my case without further comment and followed Marlene into the living room.

You often hear the phrase "unconditional love" these days, and most of the time it's pure hyperbole. But it isn't an exaggeration to use the term to describe how Marlene feels about living things, particularly the wild or semi-domesticated ones that so often run afoul of human activity. Years ago she got into the animal rescue field, first with parrots and then with almost anything else someone's cat may have literally dragged in from outdoors. No dogs or cats, but pretty much anything else. Today she lives by herself—"but rarely alone, and never lonely"—with a small collection of animals that would have perished had she not intervened on their behalf. She's deeply devoted to the idea of a "cruelty-free lifestyle." Even Lola's two massive Rottweilers are vegans, although the one she kept outside throughout our meeting looked as if he might happily become a man-eater if the opportunity arose.

A few years ago, as part of walking her talk, Marlene developed a stage character and an eco-act, then set out to help children learn to love and respect the natural world. "Eartha the Clown," she calls herself. Her act is simple, direct and very engaging, partly because it features some of her rescued animal friends and partly because it is colorful and lively. It's clear that she loves what she does as much as the animals and humans she does it for. While the act is successful, it doesn't produce enough cash to support the household. As a result, Marlene has a day-job as a real estate agent.

We first met in 2007. I stumbled across her story while searching for people who have had to deal with flood issues related to Fanno Creek. By then Marlene was nearing the end of a long, and ultimately unsuccessful struggle to save her dream home on Sylvan Creek. Mother Nature was in the process of destroying the place, and it was clear that nothing was going to stop Her. Marlene had been forced to find a second home (and a second mortgage) while she figured out what to do with the first. We sat down in the living room of the new place and while Marlene rolled out her saga, one of the Rottweilers—Sophie by name—let us take turns scratching her behind the ears.

In the early 1990s Marlene came across a home lying directly on Sylvan Creek, one of Fanno Creek's main tributaries. The location offered her an opportunity to enjoy a direct connection with wildlife without requiring a move to the country. The undeveloped and heavily vegetated floodplain surrounding three sides of the property created a strong sense of intimacy with nature. The quiet dead-end street on the east side, shared with only two other residences, did little to diminish the sense of privacy.

Marlene moved in and for the next couple years the place was everything she'd hoped it would be. Wildlife and vegetation crowded around the house and before long she and the world around her were one. Birds and squirrels flocked to her feeders, ducks and geese paddled in the nearby pond, frogs sang night and day—all within a few feet of the back deck where she sat to have her morning coffee. "I simply became part of the naturalness of it all. All the critters became quite tame and I could feed most of them right out of my hand." She gave me a sad little smile. "It was one of the best times of my life."

When the rains came, the creek would rise and the pond upstream strained against its weir, sometimes overflowing, but never for very long. Occasionally the creek would flood, and the wetlands between the creek and the house became a shallow pond as well. Once in a while, one of the few remaining Douglas firs near the site would die, an indication that the ground had become so saturated with water that only aquatic or semi-aquatic vegetation could survive there. But despite these disturbances, nothing major occurred to jolt Marlene out of her comfortable relationship with Sylvan Creek.

Then, early one morning in 1996, at the height of a rainstorm that rattled the windows, the creek came out of its banks, rolled across the wetlands, and invaded the house. On this occasion it merely worked its way into the ducting beneath the floor. The rest of the house remained high and dry. Within a day the water had subsided, and a few days after that the minimal damage had been surveyed and repaired. But the event marked the beginning of what would become more than a decade of frustration and heartbreak for Marlene.

At first, she and her nearest neighbors tried to frame the flood as being an unusual event, one unlikely to be repeated any time soon. But it *was* repeated, over and over again. During the next few years the level of damage to Marlene's house became increasingly serious. Several times each winter and spring the volume would be too much for the creek to contain, and Marlene would watch helplessly as the water level rose across the landscape, making its way up to and over the row of sandbags that now formed a soggy moat around the foundation of her home. Sylvan Creek was laying siege to Marlene's house, periodically filling up the crawl space, and sometimes even flowing across the floor.

As the flooding became more frequent, the wetness began to linger for days, even after the waters receded. Mold, mildew, and dry rot began to take their toll on more than just the foundations of the structure. She put the house on the market, but the realty business was beginning to slide. The fading market and generally poor condition of the home made the prospect of unloading it, even at a bargain-basement price, more and more unlikely.

As Marlene tried to grasp the dimensions of the situation, she became convinced that human activities up and down the stream were at the root of the problem. When she looked upstream, she saw the expansion of Highway 26 as a probably cause. In particular, she focused on the construction of the new transportation facility at the top of the Sylvan overpass area, directly above one of Sylvan Creek's main tributaries. She also came to believe that the many residential developments being carved out of the flanks of the ravine north and south of the highway were adding to the volume and silt-load carried downstream by the creek during storm events.

When she looked downstream towards the park at the end of her property, Marlene saw an additional menace: beaver dams. She and her neighbors were convinced that dams on Sylvan Creek created by beavers further to the south had started the trouble, and that subsequent efforts by the United Sewerage Authority to fix the problem had only made it worse.[71] Steps were taken, including the removal of several beaver dams; but as far as Marlene was concerned, these fixes were too late and too little. Her home was fast becoming uninhabitable.

Convinced that one or all of the developments upstream and down had played major roles in turning her dream home into a nightmare, Marlene began to complain to the various authorities involved. She also sought legal advice, and when all else appeared to fail, she went to the press. In return for her effort and her tears she received attention, sympathy, occasional loads of sand bags, and—in the end—a bit of notoriety. Real satisfaction in the form of an effective remedy remained elusive however, and by late 2007 the house had become a genuine health hazard. She would have to move out.

One bleak and dreary day a few weeks later a crew showed up to help her haul furniture out of the dank interior. She had arrived anxious and early that moving day, ready to give the crew instruction and advice if either turned out to be needed. She was also concerned about safety issues, since long exposure to the damp had fostered a great deal of mold and mildew in the interior. And then there was the problem of the huge spiders that had taken up residence in the place since she had stopped living there weeks before. They were everywhere. Something about a house full of mildew seems to attract and sustain monster spiders, Marlene once explained to me. Walking in and seeing them on the walls and ceilings gave her "the total creeps," and it took all her nerve to pass beneath them when she went through the house. Her regard for life made it impossible for her to kill them, of course. She wouldn't have used a pesticide to clear the place if someone had held a gun to her head.

The men wheeled their dollies across the rotting walkway, avoiding the weaker boards she pointed out as she carefully led the way. Then, at the door of the house, she paused. "Do either of you suffer from arachnophobia?" she asked. She was genuinely concerned.

For a moment the men look puzzled.

"Hell, lady," said the big one, "I ain't allergic to nothin' as far as I know. How 'bout you, Carl? You got aragnefobia?"

"I'm good," allowed Carl.

Marlene studied the pair for a moment. "Please be extra careful of the china," she said, and opened the door.

---

71 Virtually every watershed professional I've talked to about this situation believes that neither of these earlier dams contributed significantly, or even at all, to the flooding issues that plagued Marlene. The distance was too far, given the elevation changes that were involved.

The Elephant Factor

One of the key contributors to Marlene's ordeal is a small roadside ditch almost two miles away from her home[72]. The ditch is roughly two feet deep and four yards long. It runs along the east side of SW 57th Avenue, just below the shaved head of TV Hill. The entire hilltop has been graded, contoured and planted over with grass. A handful of communications equipment, including two massive radio towers and two smaller antennae, operate from this vantage point. It's a well-maintained area, and not a stray stem of blackberry or any other vegetation shows itself for long against the grassy expanse. The lay of the land here creates a three-acre funnel that directs stormwater runoff directly into the ditch at the roadway. The hillside is so steep in this area that building the roadway required cutting and filling the slope. As a result, the culvert carrying stormwater runoff from the ditch to the downhill side of the road is more than six feet above the graveled splash pool below. This is the birthplace of Sylvan Creek.

For roughly a third of the year not even a trickle of water issues from the culvert. During these dry times the splash pool is only a damp spot in the underbrush, if that. But all this changes—sometimes spectacularly so—when real weather comes to the hilltop. I visited this place one afternoon shortly after Marlene left her home for the last time. Just the night before, a storm had pushed through the area and dropped almost an inch of water in just under an hour. The rain came down so hard and so fast that the soil was saturated in just a few minutes. As a result, very little absorption took place at the surface. Over the next 45 minutes, the grassy area immediately below the antennas shed upwards of 58,653 gallons[73] down the slope and into the culvert.

Sometimes it is hard to conceptualize volume, so another way to think about stormwater runoff is in terms of its equivalent weight, a more accessible concept for most of us. A gallon of water weighs 8.35 pounds; 58,653 gallons weigh about 490,000 pounds. A good-sized elephant weighs in at close to 9,000 pounds. This means that in something under an hour, a mass of water equivalent to 54.75 elephants pushed its way out of the downslope end of the culvert on 57th Avenue and dropped into the little splash pool below. From there the elephants headed down hill and into the top of a deep, narrow canyon. For the next mile or so, more elephants entered the fray from adjacent slopes and side channels, sometimes in columns similar in size and force to the one that began at the top of the hill.

A conservative estimate puts the total Sylvan Creek watershed upstream from Marlene's house at roughly 700 acres. During a heavy rain event, as many as 10,000,000 gallons or 83,500,000 pounds of stormwater may run off this

---

72 The very ditch I discovered when I first scouted TV Hill while looking for Fanno Creek's headwaters.
73 The math: Rainfall = 1 inch/hour on 3 acres = .24 acre feet or 78,204 gallons at 75% runoff = .18 acre feet or 58, 653 gallons of water.

Sylvan Creek headwaters below the antenna farm on TV Hill

acreage and into the creek. That's a lot of elephants, 9,000 of them in fact; but volume is only part of the story. The slope they tumbled down averages an eight percent grade, which means that in addition to weighing a great deal, each of the elephants was traveling at close to 10 miles an hour.

When they finally poured out of the bottom of the ravine and broke out onto the relatively open plain just north of Marlene's house, they made a god-awful mess. A few of the stronger bulls kept moving and made it all the way downstream to the creek's confluence with Fanno Creek, a third of a mile to the south. Another sizeable group wandered around the open areas of the valley for a while until they were able to collect their wind and head off after the lead bulls. As for the rest, exhaustion finally overcame them. They dropped on the spot, many of them coming to their end in the flat areas surrounding Eartha's house.

Any analogy pushed far enough ultimately fails, so I won't push the elephant herd any further. My main point is this: every time a heavy rain falls on TV Hill, a water column more than a mile long and only a few hundred feet across develops between the splash pool at 57th Avenue and the valley where Marlene's house used to stand. The amount of water passing through this column in just a few hours is phenomenal. So is the amount of sediment left behind. One estimate puts the annual amount of silt deposited in the general area each year at 120 cubic yards.[74]

Causes and Culprits

Marlene was correct in assuming that events both upstream and down had set the stage for the ultimate demise of her home; but the horizon for those events extended back in time at least two hundred years. In a very real way, the fate of her home had been sealed well before the contractor decided to build in that spot. And once its foundations had been laid, little of a practical nature could have been done to save it.

Prior to settlement by Euro-Americans, the upper reaches of the Sylvan Creek watershed were covered by a dense canopy of old-growth cedars and Douglas firs. The canopy in these upper elevations was so tight and the ground below it so littered with detritus and mosses that most of the time very little water ran through the creek at all. From time to time changes in the forest or the landscape itself might create an opportunity for the little creek to become more robust. At such times it would have gone romping down the hillside, further rearranging the landscape in the process. Sooner or later, however, the canopy would refill, the carpet of detritus and moss would retake command of the land and the stream would again become a mere trickle. As a result, while

74 Clean Water Services—internal communications.

Sylvan Creek sometimes carried large quantities of silt down the hill and out onto the floor of the valley near the site of Marlene's future property, the overall siltification process was very gradual.

When the first loggers arrived and began taking down the forest, the creek's behavior began to change as dramatically as the character of the landscape itself. The soft understory vanished in a couple of seasons and the vulnerable topsoil began pouring off the hill in trainloads with every rain. As the decades went by the timbermen were replaced by land developers and builders. The hillsides were clear-cut, graded and replanted with residential dwellings and roadways. The ravines carrying Sylvan Creek and its feeders were gutted to make way for sewer systems, water mains, gas lines and all the other apparatus it takes to construct modern residential neighborhoods. These ripped-up ravines began to erode heavily and haven't stopped since.

Property development during the first heydays of residential development was not as closely regulated as it has been in recent times. As a result, many residences sit directly on the brow of the ridges along Sylvan Creek, and not a few have been built with decks and other portions perched on stilts, literally hanging over the creek beds below. The permeable surfaces that once absorbed the greatest portion of rainfall into the aquifer are now mostly relegated to the narrow shoulders and deepest gullies along the roadways that wind through the neighborhoods.

About a mile into its downhill run Sylvan Creek passes beneath Sunset Highway, an eight-lane super-slab connecting Portland to points west. The highway follows a portion of the old Canyon Road route to the Tualatin Basin. At the summit of the pass is a large highway maintenance facility built by the Oregon Department of Transportation. It was constructed on a massive fill project that buried one of Sylvan Creek's many upland feeder streams. The facility was part of the overall improvement of Highway 26 that took place between 1997 and 2004.

Below Sunset Highway the rate of residential development has been even more extreme. The stream corridor is crowded with homes, many of them built right up to the edge of the creek. Even with today's more progressive land-use regulations and construction practices, the stormwater-carrying capacity of this portion of the watershed continues to shrink. As the watershed's capacity decreases, the stream's load of water and silt increases. Every year more stormwater carrying more silt and more energy enters the top of the valley where Marlene's home once stood.

When Marlene began appealing to Sylvan Creek's various regulators for a remedy to her problem, she was going up against insurmountable odds. The physics of the situation were inescapable. The floor of the valley where her home stood would continue to be buried in silt, year after year. The rate of deposition might vary, but the process itself was built into the core functioning of the watershed. Furthermore, it wasn't clear which agency or authority was most responsible for providing her with assistance.

Her home lay in unincorporated Washington County, which meant that Clean Water Services was her sewer and surface-water management provider. But to what extent was cws culpable, if at all? Tualatin Hills Park and Recreation District (THPRD) owned the park where the beavers were going about their business. Would anyone be able to calculate the degree to which the beavers' actions might have contributed to siltification in the area of Marlene's home? Even if they could, to what extent was THPRD responsible for the behavior of wild animals on their property? The City of Portland, Multnomah County, the City of Beaverton and the Oregon Department of Transportation had jurisdiction over various portions of the watershed upstream from Marlene's place. To what extent and in what ways might they be responsible for the net siltification at her house?

Even presuming that a case for culpability could be made, or that the agencies concerned might like to see a positive solution, finding a remedy for the situation was almost impossible. Removing silt, then maintaining the area through subsequent dredging on an annual basis, would be far too costly. A single-axle dump truck, the kind that might be able to navigate the narrow streets of Marlene's neighborhood, holds six cubic yards: it would take twenty trips to haul just one year's accumulation of silt out of the watershed. Furthermore, the silt would need to be taken out uniformly to avoid creating low areas that would exacerbate the problem. Even without considering possible methods of collecting and removing the material, it was clear that addressing the problem only at the downstream site would be pointless.

Engineering or environmental solutions to the erosion issues are as scarce upstream as they are at the site of Marlene's house. Controlling stormwater runoff requires a systemic approach; in this case it would require the coordinated efforts of multiple governments and, multiple agencies, as well as the commercial and residential land owners whose properties might be involved. These efforts would need to be voluntary, for the most part; jurisdictional constraints virtually ensure that no single constituency can require others to conform to an approach they won't support. Ironically, one of the most significant obstacles to collaborative action on behalf of the property owners at the downstream site stems from the very laws enacted to protect their discretionary rights as private property owners.

Since the ground level can't go down, and since an effective fix upstream would be almost equally difficult to come by, perhaps the homes that remain in danger could go up? After the 1996 floods along the Tualatin River, many of the structures in the city of Tualatin were elevated high enough to keep them dry during high-water events. It might be possible to similarly elevate the two or three homes that appear most likely to encounter flooding issues within the next thirty or forty years. But even if elevating the homes was feasible from a technical standpoint, the cost factors would be significant; and the battle over who should bear them could be a nasty business.

It isn't possible, I suspect, to accurately project how long it will be until one of the other property owners closest to where Marlene's house once stood is faced with the same issues that overwhelmed her resources and led to the destruction of her home. However, unless action is taken quickly, a similarly sad event appears highly likely to recur, and soon: the physics and history of this portion of the watershed virtually guarantee disaster. The simple fact is that homes should never have been placed in Sylvan Creek's floodplain. But Marlene's home was built in the late 1960s, well before regulations enacted to protect the wetlands would have protected her, as well.

Postscript

Not long ago, as part of a project taking place elsewhere, Washington County acquired Marlene's property for use as a wetland mitigation site.[75] Shortly thereafter, a crew and some heavy equipment arrived and in short order tore down the house, dug up the foundation and hauled it all away. Today there's a well-vegetated wetland where the house with its sandbagged perimeter used to stand. The creek comes and goes through this wetland at will. The area was replanted with native vegetation, and every year it gets harder and harder to tell that there was ever a house here at all. I drove over to look at it the other day, just after a heavy rainfall.

The ground was mushy and partially submerged, even where the reeds were flourishing. I waded in a ways until I got close to the bed of the creek itself. The leaves on the surface of the water floated aimlessly, a sure sign that Mr. Beaver had a solid dam in place just a short distance downstream. I headed that way as quietly as possible and before long came to a freshly-chewed-off alder sapling. The piles of chips on the ground and the chiseled trunk were a bright orange. The tracks in the mud nearby were still clear of water. I had just missed seeing the critter was my guess.

It was cold but the sun was out, so I stayed awhile longer and poked around in the stands of willows that line the area and serve as the entrance to Raleighwood Park. The ends of the branches were already beginning to swell, and soon would

---

75 Typically work undertaken in order to offset damage to an environment through restoration or other methods, either on-site or at another location. It is also possible to "bank" mitigation credits in the form of cash payments.

sport a new generation of soft, gray catkins. A short distance away a tribe of kinglets chattered noisily as they moved through the soggy underbrush. Great restoration job, I thought to myself as I surveyed the area. Sure wished I had been around to watch the crew at work.

Back on the road, I turned and surveyed the scene one last time. Too bad they weren't able to leave the sign that once stood by the mailbox, I mused. I'd become used to seeing it whenever I stopped by for a better sense of what was happening in this quiet area of the watershed. The sign was a tacky old thing, just an oval shaped chunk of wood with a cartoon scene carved in it. In the center a smiling, yellow ducky swam in front of a bed of reeds. The pointy tail feathers of three other ducks stuck out of the water around her. "Eartha's Duck Pond," it had read.

Book Two:
A Million Trees

*Tree For All restoration event
at Englewood Park in Tigard*

Structure diverting stream flow from Bronson Creek and into an adjacent pond

1—Vigilance

Stream Regime

I clumped through the thick mud, my boots making an odd sucking-slurping sound with every step. Kendra looked over her shoulder at me with what could have been concern or amusement. Maybe it was both.

"You doin' OK?"

Of course I was "doin' OK." I huffed a "yes" back at her. But in point of fact I was laboring a little. We were moving over generally level ground, but occasionally had to navigate slippery stream banks and areas of deep mud. Kendra moved through these places easily, as though they were part of the concrete road we'd left moments before. Watershed Folk tend to move through a landscape with a natural grace usually associated with athletes or wild animals. No matter how broken the ground, or how clogged with fallen timber and underbrush, they navigate over the terrain without much thought or effort. Maybe it's because most of them are fit, or maybe they're just used to working on the ground; whatever it is, when they are on task they are wonderful to behold.

Kendra slid-hopped her way down the steep embankment, eyes fixed on a point across the creek all the time, and stopped a few inches from the edge. She was an athlete, I thought, very much in control of her focus and her body. I did a credible imitation of her movements, just managing to stay upright and on dry land. Thankfully, she was too preoccupied to notice my antics. She pointed in the direction of what looked like the remnants of an old rock wall. "That's it," she said. "Rip rap," she had called it, when she told me what we were going to investigate. The wall of rocks ran from the middle of the stream to the sides of the channel. Kendra pointed again, this time at a sort of keyhole-shaped aperture built into the wall. Its lower lip was just an inch or two below the level of the stream.

"That aperture serves several purposes," she explained. "First, it allows the pond to outflow when heavy rains and their runoff would otherwise cause it to overflow and maybe breach the dike on the far side. Then, during the dry season, it provides inflow so the pond is freshened on a continual basis. The rip-rap along the bank and down both sides of the ditch keeps the whole thing from washing away in heavy rains. And when the vegetation grows up, along the top of the bank and around this keyhole area, it'll look really cool."

I grinned back, then gestured towards a section of the stream a few yards downstream, where a mini-whitewater was noisily bubbling away. "What's with the rapids?"

"Well good for you!" She beamed. "That's exactly what I call this stretch, 'the Rapids!' It's one of my favorite parts of the entire project. These rocks are the top course, and it's all designed to slow down the stream, just enough to shunt part of the flow through this aperture and into the channel that leads into the lake. If you look closely, you can see that there's a pretty good pitch along here, so we've put in rocks and big wood at strategic intervals to slow the whole thing down before it has a chance to rip out the sides of the channel." Then she added with a frown, "But it isn't working properly, and too much water is going into the pond. I think we'll have to rip it out and try a different approach. Not the whole dike, but just the keyhole and channel portions." She brightened again. "But this is still one of the best parts of the project, in my opinion."

The "project" is a big one and involves an almost total reworking of Bronson Creek between Cornell Boulevard and 185th Avenue. When it is finished, almost a mile of new stream corridor will have been built. Before work got underway, this section of Bronson Creek wasn't really a creek at all. Three large ponds called the Tanasbrook Reservoirs occupied most of the area. They were linked outfall-to-inflow by very short sections of streambed. In the summer the water trapped inside these shallow lakes reached temperatures so high that the entire downstream system suffered terribly from oxygen depletion. To overcome these anaerobic conditions it was necessary to redesign the system so that these heat sinks could be taken offline. While most of the flow through the new channel will bypass the lakes, the keyhole structure Kendra and I had been studying will divert enough of a flow to ensure that a steady supply of fresh water makes its way into the ponds year round.

These reservoirs lie in the Johnson Creek watershed,[1] well to the west of Fanno Creek, but I was studying them to get a better sense of the kind of planning and work that goes into major restoration projects. Two similarly large and complex projects were slated to start in the Fanno Creek watershed in the very near future. The first would involve remeandering a quarter- mile section of the creek located in THPRD's Greenway Park, a stone's-throw from where the Fanno Farmhouse stands. The channel had been straightened at some point in the past, and as a result provides little habitat or erosion control in the immediate area. In addition to rebuilding the stream corridor, this project will restore three acres of floodplain that is currently covered with grass and requires regular maintenance. When the work is finished the area will look and function more like the natural landscape that existed here before the turn of the twentieth century.

The second large project will take place in the heart of downtown Tigard, where a stretch of Fanno Creek running from Main Street to Hall Boulevard will be rerouted, rebuilt and restored. A prominent feature of this plan is the improvement and establishment of trails, including a proposed 15-mile-long

---

1   Not to be confused with the larger and more well-known Johnson Creek that lies a dozen miles to the east, in Multnomah County.

Fanno Creek Regional Trail that will one day connect Portland to Tualatin. The redesigned stream corridor and its accompanying system of trails is the centerpiece of an ambitious urban renewal project.

These kinds of from-the-ground-up projects are among the most complex riparian enhancement projects cws undertakes, and are also some of the most heavily regulated. All three projects are subject to review and approval by the Army Corps of Engineers, National Oceanic and Atmospheric Agency, the Oregon Department of Environmental Quality, the Department of State Lands, the Department of Fish and Wildlife, and Washington County. Such projects are also subject to a great deal of public scrutiny and input. The costs involved are considerable, but in the long term they will significantly improve stream behaviors, resulting in higher water quality along their respective reaches.

Pieces of heavy equipment used to construct the basic layout were parked around the site. Tons of dirt had been dug up and moved around, and more dirt and amended soils had been brought in to build the new landscape. Rock, thousands of tons of it, had also been brought to the site and carefully placed in key areas—the rip-rapped embankment Kendra showed me was just one example. Acres of coconut matting, a mile or more of silt fence, and hundreds of wooden stakes and colorful little plastic flags had all gone into the mix. Several inches of straw covered the recently disturbed grounds. The inventory of plant materials that would soon cover this construction project was equally impressive. By the time cws completed this project, thousands of native plants would be carefully placed around the property. And then there was the investment in human capital...*Whew*, I thought. *This baby is costing a bundle.*

Kendra nodded as if she had heard me. "Yup, this is a big project and it's costing a great deal to pull off. But it will be worth it. We think this is going to make a big difference downstream, both in terms of the kind of habitat we're creating here and in the way this habitat will impact the other reaches below."

She swept her hand in a wiggly manner, tracing in the air the shape of the meanders that flowed away from us. "Once the trees we've planted along these banks take hold, we should see a significant drop in the rate of warming during the summer months. That will help establish the biota in the streambed that is needed to make the whole process run. The rocks and big wood we've built into the system should keep all this in place. As it decays, the big wood will also provide lots of quality breeding habitat for all kinds of aquatic life."

She paused a moment and shook her head. "You know," she said with a big grin, "not long ago we—us folks in the watershed management business—used to pull all these woody materials out of the streambeds so they wouldn't screw up flow characteristics. And we'd just discard them. Then we'd use concrete and rip-rap to armor the areas where we'd moved stuff around. Now we have to scrounge high and low for this kind of woody stuff. Can't get enough of it. We've learned a lot about stream dynamics in the last thirty or forty years."

As we walked towards the road I asked Kendra what she meant by "stream regime." I'd heard the term on several occasions, but until now I hadn't thought much about it. Context is everything where definitions are concerned. She paused for a moment, as professionals often do when asked to explain a term so familiar that its meaning has become more or less taken for granted.

"Think of it as the conditions that influence the way the basic physics of stream flow take place in a given environment." She turned around and waved at the acreage we'd just walked through. "Everything out there influences the stream, from weather patterns to ground features to the soil in the streambed. Everything. When nature goes to work on the stream it has all those things at its command, and it's always working towards the establishment of a kind of dynamic equilibrium among them. We try to do the same thing with our designs and our engineering, but we don't have all the tools and time that nature does. So, we don't always get it right."

She thought a moment before going on. "The important thing I've learned about managing streams is that we tend to make fewer mistakes when we coax the stream into doing what we want, rather than forcing it into positions that aren't consistent with its needs. So the stream conditions we create today are usually designed to work with the physics and the biology rather than against them. It may sound strange, but we haven't always approached these kinds of problems that way."

I asked her for an example and she looked puzzled for a moment. "Why, this whole project—every tiny little part of it really—is designed to make sure that nature does most of the work but doesn't get carried away with it in the process. Look at that piece of big wood over there on the other bank."

We were standing on the edge of the road, just above an area where the main stem of the creek passed under the roadway, then made a hard left hook towards the south end of the acreage. The flow was strong enough to create vortices on the surface of the stream. As it streamed out of the culvert, the water shot across the streambed and slammed into the root mass of an old Douglas fir. The root mass was large, perhaps eight feet across, and just as tall. A good third of it was well under water. A fair amount of dirt was still stuck in the nooks and crannies of the roots, and every once in a while the force of the fast moving water pulled off a small chunk and briefly smeared it across the surface of the stream. The force was strong enough to jiggle the entire tree, and this was obviously reshaping the embankment in which it was planted.

"You can't see it now, but the trunk attached to that root ball is almost twelve feet long. It's buried in rock and dirt, and over time the movements you see will anchor it in there for the rest of its life. It's chained to the area rather than set in concrete so that it can move a little while the water does most of the work. As it wobbles into position, the water is helping it find just exactly the right angle to allow it to dissipate the maximum amount of force from the stream without being ripped out of the wall and taking the whole embankment with it in the process. After a while its mass and the force of the water are going to come into a kind of balance. It won't move much or at all from that point on. The small plants all around it are Pacific willows. By the time the tree rots out enough to finally fail, the combined root masses of these bushes will be big and thick enough to hold the bank together all by themselves. The willows will also provide shade on the stream and stream bank and do all the other great things that vegetation does—carbon sequestering and all that stuff. We could accomplish the same structural objectives with a large concrete abutment, but it would cost ten times as much and would provide no additional benefits in the bargain." As an afterthought she added, "And it would be really, really ugly."

We stood by her jeep for a while. "Will you use the same approach on the Tigard site as you did here?" I asked. Tigard was in the midst of making some major changes to its downtown core, and a portion of the Fanno Creek channel figured prominently in that planning. We had walked the Tigard site a week earlier and she had shown me a preliminary design that included everything from completely re-meandering a large section of the channel to building boardwalks over wetlands.

"To a great extent," she nodded. "But in its own way this project has been much more complex than that one will be, particularly from the standpoint of permitting and community outreach.

"In Tigard we are mostly dealing with the city, so far as decision making is concerned. Oh, we'll be involved with other agencies too—all the federal ones and ODFW and DSL[2] for example—but we always are when we tackle projects like these, and things usually go very smoothly. But here we're on private property; so in addition to working with all the municipal and regulatory agencies we normally have to contend with, we also have to work with the property owners. A lot of our work has focused on educating them about the benefits of changing a landscape they're used to seeing on a day-to-day basis. In the end, it is all about trust, and we are fortunate to be in a good place right now where that sort of thing is concerned." She grinned. "Our public image is a lot better than it was even just a couple decades ago."

---

2 Oregon Department of Fish and Wildlife and Oregon Department of State Lands.

The Regulators

Kendra was both mentor and guide while I worked through the earliest stages of my research. Her willingness to take me under her wing saved me at least a year in research. Time and time again I would ask her a question; and more often than not, rather than answer it outright she would direct me to the appropriate resources. That really helped me feel more grounded in what I was attempting to learn. When I got really stuck, she was more than willing to help me over the bumps. For example, I once asked her to help me get my head around the various organizations that play meaningful roles in the day-to-day life of Fanno Creek. She laughed out loud. "Good luck with that!" Then, touched by my obvious bewilderment, she did her best to help me understand the byzantine manner in which the affairs of the watershed are organized and managed.

"The first thing to understand," she told me, "is that there are basically five levels of organization that can end up having a say about what goes on in the watershed. First there's the federal government group. Where Fanno Creek is concerned, that usually means the Corps of Engineers, NOAA, the EPA and the Department of Agriculture; but for another body of water it could also mean the BLM and other branches of the Department of the Interior. A lot of the time these agencies will be involved because of the salmonids that play such an important role in the economics of this region. Then there's the state group, which to some extent mirrors the federal group. We have the DEQ, ODA, DSL and ODFW for example.[3] Metro is the regional government and is involved with all sorts of things, particularly those related to planning for growth in the region. I'd include the County Commissioners in the Metro group because most of the players are the same. Local municipalities—Beaverton, Tigard, Portland, Durham, those guys—make up the fourth group. Depending upon the particular management issue, any—and sometimes even all—of these outfits may hold trump cards where decisions have to be made."

She stopped for a moment. "You getting all this? I don't see you writing anything."

I showed her the mic on my lapel. "Tape recorder." She shook her head and went on.

"Then there are the two water resource management utilities, Washington County's Clean Water Services and Portland's Bureau of Environmental Services. These are the organizations most closely involved in the direct management of your creek. They are where the rubber meets the road." She paused, then started to count on her fingers. "How many groups is that?" she asked.

"Five," I said. "Where does THPRD fit into all this?" Tualatin Hills Parks and

---

3 Acronyms used in this quote, in order of mention: National Oceanic and Atmospheric Administration, Environmental Protection Agency, Oregon Department of Environmental Quality, Oregon Department of Agriculture, Oregon Department of State Lands, Oregon Department of Fish and Wildlife.

Recreation District owns and manages a great deal of property in the Tualatin Basin, and early in my studies I recognized that the organization plays a very important role in the affairs of Fanno Creek.

"Ah, THPRD. Good question. They aren't like the other groups because they can only set policy internally. The rest of the time they have to comply with policies and procedures established by the organizations I just described. They are a powerful force and are doing a lot of interesting work that ranges across a pretty broad agenda. But only a portion of that agenda has to do with natural resources. Since they are a service district they are their own taxing authority. So they definitely have clout, but when it comes down to the nitty-gritty level of watershed management, they have to follow someone else's rules, lots of times the ones we set at CWS."

My head was spinning at the implications this kind of segmented management structure might have for the creek and the communications and joint project work needed to support it properly.

"Yes," she nodded, "it can get a little crazy, particularly since everybody has their own unique mission and their own perspective on how and why things should be planned and implemented. Consider this: CWS and BES both have detailed plans specifically for the Fanno Creek watershed. If you don't already have copies of these, you'd better get them soon. They'll give you a better feel for why things are done the way they are at the basin level. But planning that will directly impact Fanno Creek doesn't stop there. There's each of the cities, including Lake Oswego; the counties get into the act, of course, and then there's Metro, the Regional Government. You can go to their websites and see for yourself: at some level or another Fanno Creek comes up on their screens."

The look on my face made her laugh. "Like I said, it can get a little crazy, especially when you have to work your way through the various levels in order to get what you want. But you know, most of the time everyone pretty much knows how to work through any conflicts. You'd be amazed by how much collaboration takes place in this industry, voluntary collaboration. And remember, in some ways the rules are more important than the players. No matter what else may be going on, we all have to play by the rules of the Clean Water Act."

The Clean Water Act

In 1970 Washington County's population shot past 160,000; by the end of the decade it would top out at over 250,000. Areas of the Tualatin Basin in and around the Fanno Creek watershed would bear the brunt of this surge. The moratorium on new development that the state had imposed on Washington County in 1969 had been lifted after less than a year. The county's voters had approved the formation of the United Sewerage Agency (USA) and followed that up a couple months later with the passage of a 36-million-dollar bond measure to underwrite the new agency. These actions had been enough to get the state to let up on the county, but they didn't guarantee anything like real change in the structures underlying the overall management of the watershed. More stringent and comprehensive federal regulation would be required to bring about those changes.

I shudder to think what condition Fanno Creek would be in today if it hadn't been for the passage of the 1972 Clean Water Act (CWA). Before it was implemented, individual states maintained the rights and bore the responsibilities for establishing their own water quality standards and pollution controls. The federal government's role was limited to providing fiscal and technical resources from time to time, as well as managing water quality issues associated with interstate waterways. While the states were quick to exercise their authority, most were slow to meet their responsibilities. By the late 1960s, the vast majority of the nation's water resources were in serious peril. A more centralized and aggressive governmental approach to their governance would be required to save them. Enactment of the CWA marked a change from local watershed management practices to new ones based on federally mandated water quality standards and their enforcement.

Administered by the EPA, the CWA was part of a federal push to get water pollution under control in as short a period as possible. The focus was on point source pollution, i.e., pollution entering the water cycle at a specific place. Initially, those point sources were associated with the big polluters, primarily municipalities and industries. At the municipal level the major problem was perceived to be the treatment of sewage. Accordingly, the CWA came with a built-in federal grant program designed to aid in the construction of modern treatment facilities.[4] Meanwhile, industrial polluters were required to install technology and adopt waste water management practices that would result in cleaner water being discharged from their operations. Municipalities and private concerns could face stiff fines for failure to comply.

The Clean Water Act was not generally well received by the states, Oregon included. For one thing, it was perceived as yet another assault on state sovereignty. After all, this legislation came along during a period of considerable expansion of the federal government's influence and its direct control over aspects of daily life that once were under the almost exclusive governance of the individual states. The Great Society was just eight years old, and the states were reeling from the fiscal and cultural implications of new legislation impacting everything from social welfare to aircraft noise. The CWA took the stage with a host of other controversial issues of the day, including the Vietnam War, forced busing and the environmental movement itself.

---

4   Clean Water Service's Durham treatment plant was built using money from such grants.

THE CLEAN WATER ACT

Another contentious aspect of the CWA was the process used to determine water quality standards. Initially, proponents of the act focused on standards that would ensure that all water should be clean without regard for its intended use. But what does "clean" actually mean in the context of that most universal of solvents, water? The wrangling that took place over this issue very nearly doomed the CWA to oblivion from the start. In the end, lawmakers came up with a dual-standards approach to the issue that led to the bill's passage. First, organizations that discharged polluted fluids into nearby waterways would have to treat that discharge using the best available technology. Standards of this type are federally set and called "technology standards." If the discharge remained polluted after treatment by the best available technology, a second control strategy would have to be employed, this one based upon "water quality standards" developed by the state.

The process used to administer these standards is called the National Pollutant Discharge Elimination System. The system is grounded in a permitting process that specifies the technology and water quality standards to be used in controlling identified pollutants. The permit also specifies a deadline for compliance. Permits must be renewed every five years, a process that includes opportunities for public input. Responsibility for monitoring control efforts and reporting outcomes falls to the applicant. One of the key aspects of this process is that permit violations can lead to civil suits and even criminal indictments.

As Oregon moved toward compliance with the CWA, one of its first tasks was identifying bodies of water that failed to meet minimum water quality standards. Once identified, these impaired waters were listed under Section 303(d) of the Act. The water quality standards themselves were based in part on the notion of "beneficial use." The general list[5] of beneficial uses is long and broad, and includes drinking water, livestock, irrigation, industry, engineering, recreation, habitat (aquatic life) and aesthetic purposes. In some cases a body of water might need to be clean enough to provide all these beneficial uses—e.g., the Willamette River. Other waters might historically and reasonably be expected to provide only a few. Fanno Creek and two of its main tributaries made it onto the 303(d) list: Summer Creek, which flows down the southeastern flanks of Cooper Mountain, and Ash Creek, which flows westward out of the Tualatin Hills.

"Beneficial use" reflects a hard-nosed, commonsense, end-user approach to the issue of water quality control: some water resources simply need to be cleaner than others by virtue of their intended use. And by "cleaner" the law meant free of specific levels of pollutants ranging from heavy metals to bacteria.[6] These levels are called "loads." A body of water is considered in compliance

5   DEQ (1998)
6   Temperature is not considered a pollutant per se but figures significantly in the water quality regulatory process, particularly where the protection of cold water fisheries is concerned.

with the standard for a given beneficial use if it does not exceed a pre-designated, total maximum daily load of a specific pollutant(s). One of the Watershed Folk illustrated the basic concept by asking me to take a few sips from a glass of water to which she slowly added teaspoons of salt in between my sips. When I reached the point where I couldn't choke down any more of it without actually heaving she beamed. "Congratulations! You're now at your total maximum daily load of NaCl! How you feelin'?" She then began adding water to the briny solution until I could once again swallow a swig. "Congratulations again!" she said. "Now you know, in a fundamental way, what someone is saying when they tell you that 'the solution to pollution is dilution.' The whole idea of NPDES[7] is based on these two concepts."

By the time the Clean Water Act reached its 10th anniversary, the population of Washington County had climbed past 250,000 people. Most of the new growth was in the eastern portion of the Tualatin Basin and further concentrated in and around the Fanno Creek watershed. USA's Durham and Rock Creek sewage treatment facilities had come on line, and many other advancements had been made toward getting point-source pollution issues under control. But in spite of this apparent progress, the Tualatin River and its numerous tributaries remained in desperate condition.

There were multiple reasons for this disappointing turn of events. For one thing, the CWA was primarily aimed at point-source and ground water pollution; as a result, it failed to provide adequately for control of stormwater runoff.[8] Furthermore, the Clean Water Act was so unpopular with most states that it wasn't being enforced. In addition to being considered an infringement on state sovereignty, the CWA was also regarded as anti-business. Opponents claimed that compliance with the law would put companies out of business and workers on the street.[9] They also maintained it would cripple taxpayers. Finally, the EPA, the CWA's main enforcement agency, had been embroiled in one controversy after another for almost the entire decade. Its credibility had been seriously damaged by the Snail Darter Controversy that began in 1973 and went on for virtually the entire decade. The agency's very future was regularly debated in both houses of Congress. Lack of consistent political support equated to inconsistent budgets for the agency, which in turn equated to significant foot-dragging at practically every level of the process.

Arguments against the CWA and the EPA played well all over Oregon.[10] During the 1960s and 1970s the state's economy reeled from a series of short, but hard-hitting recessions. Timber and salmon were critical components of the

7 National Pollutant Discharge Elimination System
8 The act was modified in 1987 in an attempt to address this particular issue.
9 This remains one of the most persistent and fundamentally specious arguments used against developing and enforcing environmental policies to this day.
10 There may have been even greater political and industrial antipathy where the Clean Air Act is concerned.

periodically faltering economy, so there was little enthusiasm for legislation that might further hamper the immediate and unbridled exploitation of these and other natural resources. Little economic incentive was associated with implementing the non-capital side of the CWA. Rolling out the kind of major revisions to statewide watershed management practices required by the Act was a political and economic non-starter.

The lack of enforcement at the federal and state levels led to similarly limited progress at the municipal level. Organizations such as the USA could not be expected to implement policies when critical components of those policies—Total Maximum Daily Loads, for instance—had yet to be developed at the regulatory level. This widespread lack of action, combined with a circular logic that shifted blame from one level to the other and back again, essentially paralyzed compliance.

These issues began to come to a head in 1986, when a lawsuit brought against the EPA by a coalition of environmentalists led by the Northwest Environmental Defense Center forced the state's DEQ to begin developing those Total Maximum Daily Loads. The resulting legislation put new pressure on the USA to clean up the Tualatin River—after the Willamette River, one of the most heavily degraded rivers in all of Oregon. Then in 1988, the Northwest Environmental Defense Center filed a lawsuit against the USA in which it cited over 13,800 treatment plant violations. The suit was successful, and ultimately resulted in upgrades to the other sewage facilities under USA's control. The judgment also provided for one million dollars in civil penalties against the USA. This money was to be used for the establishment of a fund focused on environmental research, education and redevelopment.[11]

Over the next decade, the USA changed in many ways, partly as a result of the lawsuits, to be sure, but also because of a paradigm shift in the engineering fields and in other disciplines focused on the preservation and enhancement of water resources. The assumptions (cultural as well as scientific) that had prevailed in these fields for decades and even hundreds of years were giving way to new ideas involving a more holistic, systems-oriented approach to water quality issues. Processes were becoming more collaborative and transparent to the public. The range of decision-making criteria was extended to include not only economic and technical factors but social and environmental considerations as well. And the clear-cut distinctions that had existed between many disciplines in the past were becoming fuzzy and less constricting.[12]

11 The Tualatin Valley Water Quality Endowment Fund. A grant from this fund provided some of the start-up capital for the Tualatin River Keepers (see below).
12 Eckman et al (2000). Similar changes in organizational structure and culture were taking place at Portland's BES during the same time frame, particularly in the Watershed Management Division. As a result, the overall management of Fanno Creek today is inherently more consistent, even though it is managed by two distinct Authorities.

The Durham Plant, Clean Water Service's state-of-the-art sewage treatment plant

In 2001 the Unified Sewerage Agency was renamed Clean Water Services, a change that spoke more directly to its overarching mission and signaled a decision to move the organization further into the vanguard of its field. The Durham plant was already a nationally acclaimed success, a real award-winner. cws was now providing a higher level of wastewater treatment than 98 percent of the treatment facilities in the rest of the country, as well as the highest level of treatment provided by any of the state's 400 wastewater treatment organizations. Over the next decade, the agency would succeed in developing a reputation for holistic thinking and community outreach rivaling its growing reputation for technical excellence. Communications played a major role in cws's efforts to develop deeper ties to the basin's many citizen-stewardship groups. Without such ties the agency would have been hard-pressed to meet some of its most critical goals.[13]

Watching the Watchers Watch

There's something inherently seditious about meetings held in the back rooms of taverns. The thought crossed my mind one evening as I entered the darkened interior of Max's Fanno Creek Brew Pub and made my way to the small meeting room tucked up next to the kitchen. Max's is just a few feet from where Fanno Creek flows under Main Street in downtown Tigard. It had just reopened under new ownership and was now "a comfortable, kid-friendly, non-smoking, trans-fat-free establishment with free Wi-Fi." The new owners had made one of their back rooms available to groups and private parties. The office of the Tualatin Riverkeepers (TRK) was just a few blocks away, and the group's Citizen Action Committee met regularly at the pub. That night TRK was hosting a presentation by Rich Hunter, Water Resources Program Manager at cws. He was going to provide an update on the Healthy Streams Plan, for my money one of the most significant documents in the entire watershed library. I couldn't wait to hear what he might have to say.

The Tualatin Riverkeepers is the premier non-profit watershed group in the Tualatin Basin. It's a grass-roots organization, founded in the late 1980's from the paddling interests and environmental concerns of three independently minded Watershed Folk[14] who loved the Tualatin River and simply wouldn't let it die without a fight. The group began the way most "friends" groups do: a few individuals with a commonly felt need bonded and began to develop watershed projects they could work on together. Other like-minded folk were attracted or recruited to the ranks, enabling the group to work on larger and more diverse projects. Since then, TRK has grown from its informal origins into a powerful environmental advocacy group.

13 CWS (2005)
14 Rob Bauer, April Olbrich, Kathy Clair.

The birth of TRK and many similar groups nationwide was one of the few bright spots for the environmental movement in the 1980s.[15] Ronald Reagan took office as the decade began, and for the next eight years the prevailing winds out of Washington blew relentlessly against the movement. One of Reagan's first appointees was Portland native Donald Hodel, who became Secretary of the Interior. Time Magazine dubbed Hodel author of the so-called "Ray-Ban Plan." As a joke he had suggested that maybe the best way to deal with the ozone depletion problem was for people to wear more sunscreen. James Watt, Reagan's appointee to the Interior Department, considered the EPA an unnecessary waste of taxpayer money and was determined to dismantle any environmental programs he could get his hands on. Ann Gorsuch Burford, Reagan's first appointee to the EPA, seemed intent on stripping the agency bare. As a result the EPA spent most of the decade fighting for its existence and was generally too poorly led and/or too underfunded to fully meet its mandate.

Meanwhile the environmental movement itself was in the process of shifting its focus from the militant and confrontational tactics of the late 60s and early 70s to a more mainstream approach, one designed to attract rather than repel the broader American public. Some of the more direct-action oriented environmental activists hadn't quite caught on to this fact, however, and regularly raised hell with the establishment. For many Americans, the word "environmentalist" conjured up images of long-haired hippies wearing ragged blue jeans patched with the shredded remnants of American flags.

Stereotypes notwithstanding, the *idea* of environmentalism was becoming part of the nation's mainstream consciousness. More and more people were willing to support organizations such as the Sierra Club, Defenders of Wildlife and the World Wildlife Federation. By 1985 almost four million people were members of these increasingly mainstream groups, and they were spending more than 200 million dollars a year on environmental causes. Increasing numbers of people were also becoming active in small, grass-roots volunteer groups focused on education and restoration work at the local level. The Tualatin Riverkeepers was one of these organizations, and by the early 1990s it had grown into a force to be reckoned with.[16]

Today, TRK's mission is clear and straightforward: Work to protect and restore the Tualatin River. The organization uses many strategies to achieve its goals. Its members work to restore select sites, develop river access for paddlers, run summer camps, and engage in political advocacy, education and community outreach. The Citizen Action Committee meeting that night in Max's Brew Pub was designed with several of these strategies in mind. The

15 Kline (1997)
16 The organization received much needed startup capital from a grant provided by the Tualatin River Water Quality Endowment Fund.

number and demographics of attendees at these meetings tends to vary in accordance with the relative wonkishness of the subject matter.

One of the first meetings I attended focused on the hot topic of Low Impact Development. Almost fifty people packed into the back room for that one. They ran the professional gamut from policy-makers to practitioners. Max's sold a lot of beer and hamburgers that night. Ordinarily, however, these meetings attract only about a dozen *people*; only on a few rare occasions is the waitperson lucky enough to pocket more than a few bucks.

Brian Wegener, TRK's Watch Coordinator, is responsible for organizing and running these meetings. His background is in math and statistics, and he's held jobs in research and regulation, as well education. He's been with TRK for five years and wears many hats—webmaster, writer, researcher, advocate, field worker, educator, media specialist—you name it. One of his duties involves coordinating these Citizen Action Committees, and to that effect he was busy setting up a projector for the night's presentations.

The Healthy Streams Plan[17] was on the agenda and I hoped that topic would draw a good crowd. The process used to put the plan together is emblematic of the more collaborative approach to watershed management that has developed in the Tualatin Basin over the last several decades. More than 120 people, representing all kinds of watershed interests from ordinary citizen to County Commissioner, directly participated in the planning process. Many more were involved peripherally, through subcommittee and conference work that helped shaped the final plans.

The plan was designed by cws for use by multiple watershed constituencies as an aid to their own watershed management activities, particularly those focused on protection and restoration actions carried out within cws's jurisdictional area. I ended up with a copy of the plan after mentioning to Kendra Smith that I felt there was little in the way of a common vision at work in the management of the watershed.

"What do you mean?" she asked.

"I sometimes get the feeling," I told her, "that not all the watershed groups are on the same page. Their efforts, particularly those at the "friends" level, seem so localized and isolated; not only in perspective but also in long range strategy. At the leadership level, what's the grand plan? Or is there one?"

She turned to the credenza behind her and pulled an 11-by-14-inch spiral-bound paperback book from under a pile of papers. "Here it is. At least here's our cws perspective. Study this awhile and see if a lot of the work you're talking about makes a little more sense to you. If it doesn't, let me know and we'll talk."

It was the Healthy Streams Plan, 103 pages of some of the best and most

17 Smith & Ory (2005)

A restoration crew at work in Cook Park on a wetlands planting project for Clean Water Services

accessible watershed thinking I've come across to date. Kendra had been the plan's principal author. As she anticipated, it helped me better understand the issues and challenges involved in managing an entire watershed like the Tualatin Basin. It also gave me a better sense of the level and quality of coordination that needs to take place among the various organizations involved in that management process.

Rich Hunter, that night's presenter, was Kendra's successor at Clean Water Services and had been working in that capacity for two years.[18] He began by going over a bit of the history of the plan. Work on the plan began in 2001 and took four years to complete. The overarching goal was to come up with a plan that would be grounded in science, but also reflect the region's core values and economic needs. It was adopted by the local jurisdictions[19] served by cws in 2005.

The primary focus of the Healthy Streams Plan is the enhancement of the Tualatin Basin's surface water system, specifically the streams, wetlands, floodplains and upland buffers comprising the living portions of the watershed. The area involved includes 42 miles of the Tualatin River and more than 330 miles of streams, most of which lie within Washington County's urban growth boundary. The plan is designed to meet, and in many cases exceed current regulatory requirements established by the Clean Water Act, the Endangered Species Act, the EPA, the Corps of Engineers and the Oregon Department of Environmental Quality. As a result, addressing the impacts of non-point pollution is a major goal of the plan.

Rich then discussed projects associated with the actual implementation of the plan. The first ones he detailed were aimed at the preservation and enhancement of watersheds in urban and semi-urban areas. These included the Tanasbrook and Greenway Park projects that Kendra had schooled me on before leaving cws. The completed work is only a couple of years old, but already the changes in the habitat and the hydrology are profound. They provide excellent examples of what time, money and a holistic approach to stream renovation can accomplish.

Retrofitting stormwater outfalls and culverts is another critical component of the plan. Outfalls are places where stormwater is discharged directly into a stream—parking lots, the roofs of malls, particular spots on streets and highways. Prior to 1991, this kind of surface water discharged directly into the surface water system without treatment of any kind. After 1991, however, the cws was obligated to manage, and ultimately abate, the effects of these kinds of non-point pollution-rich discharges. The planners had identified 68 priority outfall targets, many of which were located in the Fanno Creek watershed.

18 A year earlier Kendra had left CWS for a position with the Bonneville Environmental Foundation, where she serves as the Willamette Model Watershed Program Director.
19 These include Beaverton, Durham Forest Grove, Hillsboro, Tigard and Tualatin.

They also identified a total of 581 culverts throughout cws's jurisdictional area that were deficient in terms of water conveyance, fish passage or both. At least 75 of these targeted culverts lay in the Fanno Creek watershed. Rich reported that 25 outfalls had been retrofitted and "dozens" of culverts replaced with new ones of greatly improved functionality. The plan calls for the complete retrofit of the priority outfalls and 66 percent completion of priority culvert replacements by 2015. Later, looking at the math and reflecting on everything I knew about the outfall and culvert replacement process, I had a hunch that meeting the full measure of the metrics associated with the plan was turning out to be quite a challenge for cws.

Controlling stream temperatures in most portions of the Tualatin Basin poses yet another major challenge for the agency. Uniformly they are too high for the health of many varieties of native fish and other aquatic life that inhabited the Tualatin's waters prior to the turn of the twentieth century. One relatively low-cost method of reducing these temperatures is to ensure that streams and other water bodies are as well shaded as possible. Accordingly, cws created the Community Tree Planting Challenge. The overall goal is to plant 2,000,000 trees between 2005 and 2025. Over 13,000 volunteers have contributed a total of 45,000 hours to this project. The most exciting news is that as of 2012, more than a million trees have been planted, more than half of them in the Fanno Creek watershed. Unfortunately, finding new sites for planting parties, especially the large ones that tend to have the greatest success, is getting more and more difficult; every year there is less and less unplanted land available to work on. Still, Rich is confident that this is one of the plan's "measureables" that cws and the community will exceed well before the 2025 deadline.

Going forward, Rich told us, cws will continue to focus on developing policies and programs designed to increase community involvement in surface water management, particularly with regard to stormwater runoff in urbanized areas. The approach is multifaceted and includes the creation of an Erosion Prevention and Sediment Control manual. Finally, he noted that a new program has been launched to tackle one of the most complex and urgent aspects of overall stormwater management: the development and maintenance of water quality facilities on private property.

As he concluded his talk, Rich spoke briefly about a major challenge faced by everyone in the Tualatin Basin: the regional water supply. He began talking about the dam at Henry Hagg Lake and my mind began to drift a bit. That dam was so far removed from Fanno Creek and its issues that I had a hard time focusing. More often than not in these kinds of meetings, Fanno Creek and the other degraded urban streams in the watershed are viewed as part of the problem—which they certainly are—and only rarely as part of the solution—which I feel in my gut that they are, or at least might be. These battered waterways contribute disproportionately to the degradation of the Tualatin River; so much so that I believe they hold the key to getting the water quality problem back under control.

"I'd be glad to answer any questions," Rich said as he brought the presentation to a close.

My hand went up as though it was on a string. "What's next for the plan? Will you folks be revisiting it any time soon? And if so, will there be an opportunity for public comment at that time?"

"We continue to monitor projects and update the data continuously, if that's what you mean," Rich answered. "The plan is serving its purpose and we'll be moving forward with it, even as we begin to look at other possible directions."

"What other directions?" I asked.

"Flow restoration would be one. The creeks—your Fanno Creek, for example—don't flow very well in the most critical portions of the year. We continue to look at all kinds of options that might address the stream recharge issue. We are also continuing to look at options for upgrading or re-creating natural water quality systems around the basin. We think that learning how to use natural systems to perform a lot of the work we are trying to do now with technology is the way to go with future projects."

He flipped back through his PowerPoint slides until he came to one that focused on community involvement in managing stormwater runoff. "A great many miles of stream corridor are on private property where it's impossible for us to take effective action on our own. If we can leverage more of the potential resources these out-of-bounds areas represent, we could see a significant improvement in the health of streams like Fanno Creek."

On the way home I reflected long and hard on that last point. Close to 90 percent of Fanno Creek's system of streamways and wetlands lie on a mix of residential and commercial properties. Better than 75 percent of those stream miles run through residential neighborhoods. From a watershed management standpoint, this means that upwards of 35 miles of stream corridor travels over mostly unmonitored and non-professionally managed territory. Terrible things can and do happen to the tributaries and main stem of Fanno Creek where they pass through such environs; but wonderful things can happen as well. Sometimes all it takes to get the ball rolling in the right direction is one person to take the time to learn how to manage their share of the watershed in more responsible and effective ways, and then tell their friends about it.

Portland Community Colllege/Sylvania students removing English ivy from a stand of Oregon grape

2—The Advocates

Friends Groups

As Rich indicated in his presentation, in the past cws has been able to meet some of its key performance targets in part because it's been able to harness the energy of thousands of volunteers. Most of the other major watershed management groups working on issues affecting Fanno Creek also rely on volunteers. For the most part, these volunteers belong to small, grass-roots organizations collectively known as "Friends Groups." Many of these groups are born out of the felt needs of one or two people who can't or won't tolerate the continuation of what they perceive to be an unsatisfactory situation somewhere in the watershed. Most of these small organizations are as ephemeral as some of the streams they work so hard to protect and restore; but a few have staying power and become integral partners in the formal management of the watershed. Bridlemile Creek Stewards (bcs) is a case in point.

One day Steve Mullinax decided to naturalize his section of the small creek running through his backyard. The stream was part of the drainage along the southern slopes of Council Crest,[20] the second highest hill in the Fanno Creek watershed. He knew he had much to learn about restoring native plants and natural systems, so he began looking for resources. His research led him to the Bridlemile Neighborhood Association and a watershed partnership with Greg Schifsky that lasted well over a decade. In the beginning bcs focused on a few neighborhood properties, helping the owners to restore their sections of the watershed. This led to more complex activities; festivals, monthly watershed maintenance events, and a greater involvement in Portland city properties, such as Hamilton Park.

Once Hamilton Park was somewhat in hand, Steve and Greg turned their attentions to Portland's Albert Kelly Park. A small stream runs through the heart of this 12.5-acre property and its corridor was in bad shape before bcs went to work on it. Armed with a $5,000 grant from the Bureau of Environmental Services and the cooperation of Portland Parks and Recreation Department, the group went to work pulling out invasive plants and replanting the area with a selection of native plants and trees. In 2005 bcs received the prestigious Green Heron award from the Tualatin Riverkeepers, partly for the quality of their projects at Hamilton and Albert Kelly parks.

Today bcs operates under the banner of the Southwest Neighborhoods, Inc., a non-profit group of 17 neighborhoods located mostly in the hills southwest of downtown Portland. Funding for Southwest Neighborhoods, Inc. comes from the City of Portland and from fundraising activities conducted by the organiza-

20 For more about the colorful past of this important Portland landmark, visit http://www.pdxhistory.com.

tion itself. The BCS has evolved from being an informal, loosely knit group of neighbors to a formally structured committee operating within a large, volunteer-based organization. This evolution has provided both the fiscal and human resources necessary to manage large-scale projects. It's also helped BCS find a way around the administrative, financial and succession challenges that so often doom grassroots volunteer organizations to eventual oblivion. Not all of the watershed's friends groups have been so lucky.

No friends group better exemplifies the ups and downs of volunteerism than the Fans of Fanno Creek. Always informal; always driven by the passions of a handful of people; always fiercely dedicated to the environment in general and Fanno Creek in particular; always independent as hell; and always a little bit quirky and unpredictable—that's been the Fans of Fanno Creek throughout its history. Most of that history is unwritten, so getting a real feeling for the exact details of its overall development is a little difficult. Some aspects of its earliest activities may be more mythical than factual. For example, it's rumored that a few of the original members operated in something close to the Edward Abbey tradition,[21] particularly where the protection of beavers and beaver dams were concerned. When I've tried to pursue that informational thread I haven't been able to get very far. "I have no idea what you're talking about," one nameless source told me. "And who's this guy Edward Abbey you're talking about?" he smirked.

Mythological considerations aside, for almost twenty years Fans has been one of the most respected friends groups in the Fanno Creek watershed. They've successfully addressed physical issues, like restoration work, and engaged in the political arena, giving testimony on land use policies or practices. The group has been able to be so effective because its board knows how to harness the diverse capacities of its loosely knit constituency.

The Fans also walk their collaborative talk by being one of the most consensus-oriented groups I've ever seen in action. Although there's a board of directors, it exists primarily because when the group became a 501(c)3 corporation they discovered that they needed one. Democratic to the core, Fans scrapped the hierarchical notion of a president and vice president, opting instead for two co-presidents. There's also a secretary and a treasurer, one of whom also serves as the group's webmaster. The Fans have no formal process for bringing issues or projects to the table; just show up and speak your piece. There's typically an agenda, but that gets quickly shoved to the back burner whenever a citizen shows up with a watershed issue needing immediate attention. That's how I ended up becoming a member.

---

21 Abbey was the author of the *Monkey Wrench Gang*, a novel that provided inspiration to Earth First, a radical environmentalist group that has been embroiled in controversy since it was founded in 1979.

I guess I'm a member. I don't have a membership card or any of that kind of authentication, but I suspect that as long as I show up from time to time I'll be bonafide. At any rate I was just getting started with my research and wanted to connect with a Friends Group to see how they operated. I'd sent out feelers among the few Watershed Folk I already gotten to know and every one of them said something to the effect, "Oh, you'll want to talk to Fans of Fanno Creek for sure."

After calling ahead to make sure it would be okay to stop by and talk to the group about my book project, I received a warm welcome when I stepped through the door. The meeting lasted a couple of hours, and most of it was devoted to me and my project. By the end of the evening I had learned a great deal about the group, which had been my intent from the beginning. But I'd also learned a lot about my environmental biases and my vast ignorance of almost all things watershed.

Earlier in the day I had visited Raleighwood Park. The visit was intended to be a test run for the journaling and photo-documentation approach I planned to use in my research. It was my first visit to the park as well as my first organized "expedition" into the urban bush. I drove past the park's entrance twice before realizing that the small patch of gravel jammed between two residences was actually the main entrance. The parking area ended in a patch of waist-high weeds festooned with pretty blue flowers. I recognized the plants right away: *Cichorium intybus,* aka wild chicory.

Back when I was a kid growing up in Arkansas, my mom tried to dry the roots of plants similar to these and grind them up to use as a coffee substitute. After a ton of work she had managed to extract an ounce or two of orange fluid. She gingerly sipped, then swirled it in her mouth. A split second later she spat it out and chugged a glass of water. "Those people in Louisiana must be crazy!" she muttered.

It made me smile to remember the incident, but I swapped that grin for a frown when I began to study the area immediately west of the entrance. The ghost of an old pathway led from the parking lot downslope and into a dense wall of brush and trees that looked nearly impenetrable. The only other indication that you might actually be able walk around in the park was a "Dogs on Leash" sign showing the outline of someone picking up after their dog.

I was puzzled and unimpressed. Where were the amenities typically found in most parks? Where were the garbage cans and paved pathways and playground equipment? I knew from looking at my map that this was a fairly large park, big enough for tennis courts and a basketball court. But all I could see for as far as I could see it was a solid wall of dense vegetation. Somewhere in that mess lay Sylvan Creek, or so the map said. In I went. The pathway gave out the instant I entered the tangle. Everywhere I turned there seemed to be thorns ripping away at me. It was mid-summer and while I was well-shod, I wasn't heavily dressed: just jeans and a light-weight cotton shirt. Within the first dozen steps my arms had been shredded by some of the densest tangles of wild roses I'd ever encountered.

Deeper into the jungle I went, heading west towards the creek, as near as I could tell. The next thing I knew, I was ankle deep in ice-cold water. I'd pushed through a wall of some kind of brush—willows I thought—and in a careless instant had stepped down into a narrow channel of water. I'd have fallen down, I suspect, if it hadn't been for all the shrubbery that crowded the stream. I looked down toward my submerged feet. This 6-inch deep stream couldn't be Sylvan Creek. It was way too small. I thrashed onward until the bushes became so closely interwoven that the only way forward would have been on my hands and knees. The ground was getting mushier with every step. There was no way I was going to crawl around on the ground in this kind of muck. I turned around and fought my way back to the truck.

That was the day I showed up to my first meeting of the Fans. The organization holds most of its meetings in the old Fanno Farmhouse in Greenway Park. It's a wonderful old building, still in the process of being fully restored. Most of the downstairs is completed, but the upstairs remains in need of finish work. The building is owned by the Tualatin Hills Park and Recreation District and is a popular venue for public and private meetings and special events. Several board members were already comfortably seated around folding tables crowded together in a square. There was room for eight more people, more room than necessary as it turned out. Introductions began.

"I'm Joe," said the first board member, introducing himself. "I'm the one you talked to on the phone the other day."

There was laughter from the other board members. "Joe is president for life," one of them said. Joe grimaced and told me about his regular work as a middle school teacher and his work as a board member of THPRD. Then he introduced me to the rest of the Fans. As luck would have it, all of the active board members were in attendance that night.

Brad, the other president-for-life, has a tech background and handles the digital support work for a local prep school. The school's grounds are home to an 18-acre, high-quality marsh, one of the largest intact wetlands in the middle reaches of Fanno Creek. Brad's interests are focused mostly on restoration work.

Linda was next. She had been on the board for "more years than I can remember." Her expertise is site restoration. She and her husband live right on the banks of Fanno Creek, in one of the neighborhoods at the base of the Green Hills area. One of the things she likes best about their particular place on the stream is that it feels like the country, even though it's just a few hundred feet from the Beaverton-Hillsdale Highway, one of the busiest roads in the entire Fanno Creek watershed. "We have coyotes," she grinned, "lots of them! The more coyotes, the fewer cats. The fewer cats, the more birds!"

Sitting next to Linda was Jay, a former U.S. Forest Service agent. He claimed to be as busy in retirement as he had been when he was still employed. He was working on his own book, a field guide to the plants and trees of the Fanno Creek watershed, and suggested we get together and share notes sometime. Part of his work involved hiking the contours of all the sub-watersheds in the Fanno Creek system. He was curious to know if I'd been to Hiteon Creek, a small tributary in the southwest quadrant of the watershed. I had no idea there was such a creek. He laughed and grabbed my map. "It's tiny and beat up in places, but it feeds into the west side of Fanno Creek down in Greenway Park, not far from *here*." He pulled a spare pin out of the side of my board and stuck it into the place where Brockman intersects 135th in Beaverton. I was thrilled to have yet another tributary to work on.

Dave, the next in line, had nearly broken my hand when he shook it. He's worked for the U.S. Fish and Wildlife Service for a dozen years. Before that he was with Metro for another dozen. His main area of technical expertise is geography. He was a Geographic Information Systems analyst during his years with Metro and holds a similar, but supervisory, position with the Fish and Wildlife Service these days. In addition, Dave is a consummate outdoorsman; I later found out that we share a deep love for the mountains and canyon-lands of southeast Oregon. Naturally enough, he handles webmaster duties for the Fans.

Last to be introduced was Sue, a wildlife scientist who lives in Tigard. The majority of quality wildlife habitat remaining in the Fanno Creek watershed lies along Tigard's portion of the creek. Sue is one of the most passionate defenders of the wildlife and the watershed habitats it depends upon. Over the next couple of years we would run into each other frequently, more often than not at the public testimony portions of planning commission or city council meetings.

That night the group had a very small agenda, most of it focused on routine organizational housekeeping, and they moved through it in short order. Then Joe turned to me. "So," he said. "You're working on a book about Fanno Creek. Why Fanno Creek?"

No one laughed, which I took as a good sign. But the question caught me a little off guard; at that point I wasn't totally sure, myself. More accurately, I hadn't been able to explain my quest/vision/project in terms that didn't sound awfully flaky, even to me. I didn't want to say that I was answering a calling (which I was). That sounded somehow smug and self-righteous. And I didn't want to say I was just doing it for fun (which I was). That might make me sound like a complete dilettante (which I might be). But I had to say something, so I focused on what I knew about the creek.

"From what I've been able to determine so far Fanno Creek is one of the most heavily regulated streams in Oregon," I explained. "That all by itself makes it interesting enough to warrant a case study. But the creek has also played a major role in the settlement of this portion of the state, and that history is important as well. Right now the 'story' seems to be developing from the jurisdictional side. My instincts have been telling me that with all the various interests and mandates at play in the watershed, the governing process might be a little dysfunctional, at the level of the streambed, at least." Lots of nodding accompanied that last comment. Encouraged, I went on.

"What I'm hoping for tonight is to get a sense of how groups like yours fit into the governance puzzle. For instance, just exactly what does Fans of Fanno Creek—you guys—*do*?"

They looked around at each other. Joe took the lead. "We mostly focus on restoration at just a couple sites these days, Bauman Park in particular. From time to time we get asked to look at land use issues; Black Bull, for example."

I hadn't heard of Black Bull, I confessed.

Sue Bielke went over the basic details. "It's a property down in Tigard that has an interesting history; I'll tell you about it someday when we have a little more time. The bottom line is that someone is trying to build a road to it, which would be no big deal, except that the road will have to run right through the floodplain and over a wetland. We've weighed in with the planners in Tigard and with the Department of State Lands. So far it looks like the wetlands is safe, at least for a while, but we'll just have to wait and see.[22] Ash Creek flows into that area," she added. "Have you looked at Ash Creek yet? It's listed as a 303(d) site with the DEQ."

I was scribbling away like mad and beginning to feel a little overwhelmed. Brad was sympathetic. "Yeah, there's way too much to learn," he said. "We've all been at this for years, lots of them, and we're still way behind when it comes to all the regulatory stuff. Speaking for myself, I try to stay out of all that and leave it to the policy wonks to work it out. I focus instead on making a physical difference in the creek's life. Sue is great about getting out there and fighting city hall. I don't know how she stands it."

"Well, somebody has to do it," Sue said. There was more head nodding. It was getting late, so I changed the topic and by asking what was up with Raleigh-wood Park. Ten pairs of eyes were suddenly focused intently in my direction. "What do you mean?" asked Joe.

"I visited the place today and was amazed by its crappy condition."

---

22 The Fans of Fanno Creek website reports that in 2008 the DSL gave the owners permission to proceed with their fill permit. The road that is being built there is part of a project called The Refuge At Fanno Creek.

You could have heard a pin drop. Joe looked genuinely concerned. "Has someone dumped a load of trash in there again?"

I gave them a blow-by-blow description of the afternoon's adventure, including my inability to discover anything that looked remotely like a creek. For a moment there was total silence as the Fans all looked at each other. Then, as if on cue, they all started laughing.

Sensing my confusion and embarrassment, Joe put one hand on my shoulder while he used the other to wipe his eyes. "Eric," he said, "we've been working on that park for more than seven years just to make sure it would end up looking exactly like that!"

After the group settled down, Joe graciously gave me a little schooling. "First off, I'm on the board at THPRD and you've given me some much-needed ammunition for getting a new signage program going for the district. That park is what we call a 'natural area.' We just don't have signage there that makes it clear what visitors should expect. Raleighwood Park is one of our greatest success stories, at least where restoration work is concerned. A few more years and it'll look a lot like it looked when the Kalapuya Indians lived here."

"You know what he should do?" Brad said to Joe. "He should join us for the restoration work we're going to do at Bauman Park next month." Agreement was unanimous and the meeting began to break up. At the door I turned back to thank them once again, then apologized for my confusion over Raleighwood. Linda patted me on the arm maternally. "Don't worry," she said. "It takes a village…"

Restoration 101

It was a miserable day for working outdoors. It had been raining more or less steadily for a couple of days; serious rain, the Pacific Northwest kind, less bombastic than relentless. For hours, even days at a time, this kind of rain can flow over the land like a vast, thin lake. It can breach virtually any system of waterproofing known to mankind. But it is the source and the hope of all that is Oregon west of the Cascades and sooner or later you learn to love it, or leave. After more than a quarter century in the Pacific Northwest I was still not fully adapted to Mr. Gray, but I was working on it. So, as the first icy threads of Oregon's life blood began working their way into the tiny gaps between my rain jacket and my neck, I pretended not to notice. "Gotta get some quality Gore-Tex®," I muttered to myself.

I slogged into the staging area near an opening in the park that passed itself off as "the entrance." I had visited Bauman on a scouting trip a few weeks earlier, shortly after the Fans invited me to join their first restoration work of the season. I like to check out a place before I photograph the activities involved, if I can. It had been warm and sunny that day; one of those pre-autumn after-

"Blackberry Park" given a face-lift and a name change—Bauman Park

noons that are so beautiful it nearly breaks your heart. I had fallen for the place immediately. It's a mess so far as the vegetation is concerned, and at seven acres it isn't all that large; but the arrangement of the terrain makes it feel much larger. To borrow from a phrase we used to use in the photography business, the place isn't pretty but it has great bones.

A lot had changed in the intervening weeks besides the weather, especially in this end of the property. A portable potty perched on a small trailer just inside the entrance. A few feet away a white fold-out table had been set up., Some kind soul had covered the top of it with cartons of hot Starbucks coffee and cocoa, along with several boxes of Krispy Kreme donuts. Below the table and somewhat sheltered from the elements were paper goods—toilet paper, cups and napkins— and a bucket full of dry cotton work gloves. Joe, Brad and Linda were guarding the table and they greeted me warmly as I slogged into the park. Linda handed me a clipboard. "You'll have to fill out this volunteer form before you can have any coffee," she teased. "We keep track of the hours volunteers put in when they work with us. Comes in handy whenever we apply for grants." I commented on the quality of the spread. "Wow, what a bunch of goodies. Great coffee."

"You'll earn it," said Joe. "Melissa, the volunteer coordinator for THPRD, pulled all this together. I don't know how she does it, but this is what it looked like when I drove in at 7:30 this morning, and the donuts were still warm." As we wolfed down multiple doughnuts and slurped hot coffee and cocoa, I voiced my concerns about the impact the weather might have on the morning's work. Would anyone else even show up in all this rain, I wondered? The three of them stared at me as if I was crazy.

"The weather's almost perfect," Joe said, without a smile, "although it would need to be much colder if we were actually planting bare-root today."

"This is as good as it's going to get," said Linda, grinning from ear to ear.

Brad nodded in agreement, crossing his eyes for a moment to focus on the drops of rainwater dripping steadily off the bill of his cap and onto the lid of his coffee cup. "You'll get used to it. This is nothing, believe me. Wait until February." I could wait, I decided.

I have since learned that miserable weather is the handmaiden of restoration work. I can count on one hand the number of times I have accompanied one of these volunteer groups into the bush without coming home wet and numb from top to toe.

There are three reasons why the period October to March figures so large on the calendars of volunteer groups engaged in restoration work. Most shrubs and trees need to be in their dormant phases when they are moved from the nursery and into the field. This reduces the incidence of loss from disease and insects. Putting them into the ground during the wettest months of the year also gives them a running start at root development before they have to en-dure the short, but usually tinder-dry season that typically lasts from late June to mid-August. An amazing number of school-age children work on these field projects, so the availability of this group of volunteers is also a significant scheduling consideration.

A few yards away from the table, more than two hundred plants in one- gal-lon containers were arranged by species into a half-dozen groupings. These turned out to be some of the native plants more commonly used in the restora-tion of riparian corridors in this area: Douglas fir, Oregon grape, Pacific willow, red osier dogwood and Pacific dogwood.

"These are from a local resource," Joe said, more than a trace of satisfaction in his voice. "A real problem for a lot of restoration work, particularly the work done by churches, scout organizations and other non-professionals, is that sometimes the folks handling the projects aren't very knowledgeable about the task. You can tell by the kind of stocks they end up using. Doug fir, for ex-ample, has an extensive range and will adapt to all kinds of microclimates and elevations. But if you take one that grew up in a nursery in the foothills of the Cascades and plant it here, in what is essentially a part of the Willamette Basin, well, it may not make it; or if it does, it may never be very strong. That's one of the reasons why a lot of volunteer work ends up being a bit of a wasted opportu-nity. Lots of times, for budget reasons, they have to take what they can get, and that's not always local stock."

Not far from the ranks of plants, several contractor-grade wheelbarrows lay upside down on the ground. Two five-gallon utility buckets nearby were filled with an assortment of long-handled cutters and plant shears. Brad motioned towards these, then toward a huge pile of brush stacked in the center of the clearing. "This is understory we needed to clear out from between the trees so we could actually plant in here. Professional crews cut all this down, but one of jobs today is to cut it into chunks that will fit into a truck." He pointed to an area further into the park. "We also need to finish cutting the underbrush out of that area. See that pile of old stuff back in there? We'll need to cut that up and haul that out as well."

"What about the plants?" I asked.

"That's Linda's baby. See the little blue flag tied to that small Doug fir over there? We planted that tree last year. When we put them in the ground we tie a flag to them, so the next restoration crew will see them. Otherwise they might get trampled. Before she finishes today she'll have put similar flags on every one of those plants. We won't actually plant them today; there's another group coming in next weekend to do that. By doing this first step we'll save them a great deal of time."

The first volunteers arrived, a pair of dad-and-daughter teams. I studied the two girls who, like everyone else but me, seemed completely unconscious of the rain. Neither wore a hat, and in minutes their hair was completely wet. In spite of that, they grinned and laughed their way through the entire morning's work. What sort of inducements had it taken to get them out of the sack and into rain gear at such an early hour and on such on such a dismal day, I asked? They looked at each other self-consciously, then simultaneously giggled and shrugged their shoulders. "Extra credit in science class," said the taller of the two. "I've been doing this since I was in grade school," said the other with a certain air of moral superiority. The dads beamed away at their rosy-cheeked offspring and I decided that they were all half-crazy. Either that or they were simply native Oregonians. I was convinced that nothing else could account for their blasé attitude towards the constant rainfall.

A few other volunteers arrived. They seemed oblivious to the rain as well. This apparently constituted a quorum because Joe thanked everyone for coming and began to outline the morning's agenda. That day the focus was on preparing several areas of the park for a succession of plantings that would take place throughout the coming winter months. A few weeks earlier a professional work crew, armed with chain saws, had bucked the largest tree trunks and limbs and hauled them to a brush pile in the clearing by the entrance. However, the bulk of the trimmings had been left where they had fallen, and today we would haul this material out of the woods, cut or break it into chunks short enough to fit into a dumpster and stack it on the pile. "Any questions?" asked Joe. There weren't any, so we all got to work.

Each of the girls grabbed a pair of brush cutters and headed toward a downed alder near the brush pile. In minutes they reduced the smaller limbs to manageable lengths and began hauling them away. The men spread out through the brush looking for bigger wood, which they tackled using small cross-cut saws. Linda rounded up a roll of blue tape and began tying flags to each of the hundreds of container plants. I followed Brad into an area where several smaller trees had been dropped on top of each other. We went to work separating their tangled limbs so we could get at them with the saws. I focused on that operation while Brad began the more difficult task of cutting the trunk sections into eight-to-ten-foot lengths. He pulled a small folded saw from the holster at his belt.

"Ever see one of these? They are *amazing*," he said. He quickly cut the four-inch limb he was holding into short sections—one, two, three, just like that! I asked if I could try it; after the first cut swore I would get one for myself the next day.[23] I cut a couple more sections while he took a short break, then went

23 The Fanno Saw Works in Chico California, which is owned by one of Eugene Fanno's descendants, produces saws of a very similar design that are used in the arbor and fruit industries.

BOOK TWO   125

back to hauling brush into the clearing. One tangled patch of tree limbs was badly locked together, so I asked Brad to pull on one end while I pulled another. As the tangle separated, several clumps of bright green ferns appeared. The color of the foliage was particularly intense.

"Hey, that's licorice fern!" exclaimed Brad. "A big patch of it! What's it doing on the ground?" He was quite excited by this discovery and called Joe and Linda over to look at it. They clearly shared his excitement. Joe brushed away some of the oak leaves piled around the plants, revealing the sodden form of a fallen oak limb. "Licorice fern, all right," he said. "The cutting crew must have dropped it here when they were working." Maybe it was my blank stare, or maybe it was the fact that I wasn't as obviously elated as everyone else, Joe realized that I didn't get it.

"It's *Polypodium glycyrrhiza*, the licorice fern, and it's not all that common," he explained. "It's used a lot in naturopathy for all sorts of things, kind of like an aspirin. The Kalapuya Indians used it."

"Does it really taste like licorice?" I asked, crushing a few leaves between my fingers. I couldn't smell anything, probably because my nose was so cold that I could no longer feel the end of it with my fingers.

"The root does, but if you chew it when it's fresh it'll make you sick," he said.

After a few more comments about this great find, we all went back to work. Ten minutes later I stopped for a moment to drink some water. As my eye wandered over the clearing, I noticed another patch of brilliant color, this one up in the canopy. It was the top of a small oak tree, maybe a dozen feet tall and four inches wide at the base. Ironically enough it was growing right next to the clump of licorice fern and we had been standing under it the whole time we discussed that find. Most of the leaves were a lovely lime green, but with the approach of deep autumn several had turned to soft shades of orange and red.

"Hey, Brad, what kind of oak is this?" I asked.

Saw still in hand, Brad walked over and peered up into the canopy.

"I don't know," he said. Then, after a moment's hesitation, "But whatever it is, it's not native."

A few quick strokes later the top of the tree hit the ground. I stared at the brightly colored mass, then at Brad.

"That was a perfectly good tree!" I exclaimed in unabashed amazement.

He shrugged. "It's not a white oak, not a native plant. We can't let these kinds of invasives establish even a toehold in here. Especially something like an oak. These things multiply faster than rabbits. The invasives in this park are bad enough already."

He returned to his work and I went back to hauling brush. It took a while to get back into the swing of it. I was a little shaken by the suddenness of the tree's removal. I noticed a couple of other interesting stands of trees during the remainder of the morning, vegetation I was curious about, but decided to avoid calling attention to any of them for fear I might be signing their death warrants.

Blackberry Park

When Watershed Folk here in the Tualatin Valley talk about watershed restoration they almost always speak from the same perspective where vegetation is concerned: out with the new, in with the old. The assumption underlying almost everything associated with the watershed's plant and animal communities is that whatever may have occupied the waters, skies and grounds of Oregon prior to Settlement is what should be here today—that and that alone. I'm convinced that some of the native Oregonians among the Watershed Folk would, if they could, extend that bias to those of us who didn't have the good fortune to arrive here still half-covered with amniotic fluid. They can't really be blamed for this bias, particularly where invasive species are concerned. The damage to Oregon's ecoregions[24] brought on by an ever-increasing variety of ecologically aggressive, non-native plant and animal species is cause for real concern. Bauman Park could be a poster child for this problem.

The park is located along the middle reaches of Fanno Creek, not far from the intersection of Oleson Road and the Beaverton-Hillsdale Highway. It would be wonderful to know what this seven acres of hammered terrain actually looked like in the pre-Settlement era. Its varied terrain and the nearby marshy areas suggest that it once formed part of an uplands area adjacent to a large swamp that stretched west from this area for several miles. Over the last 150 years, multiple waves of transportation, residential and commercial development have fragmented the area to such an extent that it represents one of the most abused areas in the watershed. For decades, a small waste treatment facility located in this area continually pumped minimally treated sewage directly into Fanno Creek.[25]

I distinctly remember riding by Bauman Park shortly after I moved here in 1997. Dense stands of blackberry had overtaken the area and in several places hung well over the road. I was on a motorcycle at the time, and oncoming traffic made me stay well inside my lane. As I swept around a curve, several blackberry canes reached out and shredded the right arm of my leather jacket.

24 Ecoregions are roughly analogous to watersheds, except that their boundaries are determined by the distinct groups of flora and fauna they contain, rather than by their physical contours and/or common drainages.
25 Prior to the formation of the Unified Sewerage Agency in 1970, the degree to which the outfall from any of the half-dozen sewage plants on Fanno Creek was treated ran the gamut from hardly to somewhat. In general, most sewage received at least primary treatment, meaning that most of the solids were removed prior to dumping the effluent into the creek.

The park's neighbors called it the Blackberry Patch at the time, but I gave it a different epitaph that day. Unfortunately for the park, blackberries were only a small portion of the non-native vegetation plaguing the place. You can add English ivy, teasel, non-native hawthorn, garlic mustard, laurel, thistle, herb Robert and reed canary grass to that list, just for starters.

Joe and the rest of the Fans had been working on the park for almost a decade, and while they had made progress in some areas, the going had been slow and unsustainable. There was too much noxious vegetation for a small group working on an occasional basis, without power tools or herbicides, to overcome. Indeed, much of the work accomplished a few years earlier had become overgrown with one or more of the invasives that seemed to have no natural enemies to slow them down.

While the invasives were flourishing, the Fans of Fanno Creek were beginning to fade. Joe had been working on restoration projects and sticking up for Fanno Creek for more than a dozen years. The rest of the board had invested similar amounts of time. In January of 2008, just a few months after I participated in the Bauman restoration project, I learned that the Fans board was looking into ways to better handle the administrative chores associated with running a 501(c)3 corporation. Full-time employment combined with the work associated with Fans was becoming a heavy load for everyone. A few members were also growing tired of having to deal with the support issues associated with putting restoration and other kinds of work crews into the field. Unlike most of the Fans' other activities, projects in Bauman Park had been coordinated by THPRD. Otherwise someone from Fans would have had to handle the organizational chores. Most of the board thought it might make sense to give up their tax-exempt status and, like Bridlemile Stewards, become part of a larger organization that could support their field work.

There were several major problems with this idea, however. For one thing, no organization in the Washington County portion of the watershed was remotely similar to Southwest Neighborhoods, Inc. The only environmentally oriented organization possibly large enough to absorb the Fans was the Tualatin Riverkeepers; but because of the devastated economy, that group had more pressing concerns at the time. Perhaps, one of the Fans suggested, Clean Water Services would be interested in using their group as a nucleus for a west-side version of Southwest Neighborhoods. But the idea of being supported by an agency, or any other governmental organization, was a non-starter for most of the group. Autonomy had always been important to the Fans, and in the end they were unable to contemplate losing it.

Throughout its long history, the Fans had pretty much called its own shots. Its board had always been well-known for being willing to take a stand on critical watershed issues, but less willing to compromise once that stand was taken. While the current group was perhaps a little more collegial than others may have been, they were not above being pugnacious if and when circumstances required. The Fans could—and occasionally would—throw a metaphorical monkey wrench into the machinery of private enterprise or municipal government. This was not always appreciated in some circles; but it was, and always had been, one of the group's most valuable characteristics where Fanno Creek's health was concerned. If they disbanded it would be a blow to Fanno Creek in general and Bauman Park in particular.

The Tualatin Hills Park and Recreation District Connection

A dreary mix of rain and snow pelted the windshield, letting up just a bit as I turned onto Old Oleson Road and came to a stop under the canopy of fir trees surrounding the north entrance to Bauman Park. I pulled on my stocking cap, switched from leather driving gloves to woolen mittens, grabbed my camera, and climbed out of the car. The shock of the windblown snow against my face made me recoil. For a moment I considered getting back in the car and forgetting all about my mission for that morning. I hate being cold and wet; if I ever get lost in a snow storm I'm sure I will die of pure misery long before hypothermia has a chance to do its worst.

Still, while the weather was miserable for me, it was nearly perfect for the restoration work taking place in Bauman Park that week. Several dozen large trees would be planted here over the next few days, and the nasty weather would go a long way toward ensuring that a high percentage of them would survive. I couldn't miss an opportunity to observe the planting process and perhaps talk to the professional restoration crew that would be doing the work. I cinched up the collar of my jacket and set out for the planting site.

My route took me along the north end of the park and through an area that I've come to call "the Classroom," the place where, two years earlier, Brad had given me one of my first and most important lessons in the care and handling of invasive species. As I passed the area, I almost failed to recognize the stump of that invasive oak I'd mourned so naively back then. Had the clumps of licorice fern next to it not caught my eye, I might have passed it by.

Brad had cut it off straight across, about three feet from the ground. Now a dozen or so tall, wispy new limbs formed a crown around the top of the stump. They arched upward eight feet or more, reaching toward the canopy. Shocks of dead leaves still hung from the boughs. The oak had survived the amputation of its entire upper story and had come back with a vengeance. For a split second I found myself wondering if it could be killed simply by cutting it off every year; or would the use of poison be a more preferable method of eradication? I

A restoration crew wrestling with both the weather and plants in Bauman Park

laughed out loud. Man, had I changed! Two years ago I had been stunned by seeing the tree come down; and now here I was, trying to figure out the best way to permanently remove this evil phoenix from the Bauman ecosystem.

A rapid string of Spanish swearwords from somewhere to the southeast broke the silence. I hurried on to see what had provoked the colorful outburst. As I stepped into the cleared area along Oleson Road, one of the restoration crew was just pulling himself out from under a large, ball-footed Douglas fir that had apparently rolled down the hill, taking him with it. He must have slipped on the snow-covered slope leading from the roadside to the planting area. Everyone was laughing, even the man lying in the snow at the bottom of the hill. A fourth man appeared from the tree line at the base of the incline. He began to spin the tree on its axis, angling it towards one of a dozen or more pre-dug holes. This skillful worker turned out to be the lead crewman, Jesus by name. I explained what I was up to, then asked if he or any of his crew objected to my taking pictures of them at work. There were no objections, so I went to work documenting the process.

The trees were going in as part of mitigation for work that the Oregon Department of Transportation had performed along the nearby roadway. As is so often the case in restoration work, physical access to the heart of the site was severely restricted. The closest point was on the recently completed shoulder along the roadway, which sloped steeply towards the wooded area below. There was just enough room to park a truck on the crest of the slope. Each of the trees and its root-ball easily weighed several hundred pounds. Simply dropping them over the side of the truck might have caused the canvas-covered root-balls to burst, so the crew leaned a plank against the side of the truck as an impromptu ramp, then jockeyed them down to the ground. Once positioned on the crest of the hill, the trees were tilted onto their sides and rolled down the slope. It was this last part of the process that had sent man and tree careening down the steep slope.

The majority of the trees were conifers, Douglas firs and the like; but a few were deciduous trees, primarily alder and ash. The plan called for a dense planting pattern that would accomplish multiple goals. If the trees survived, they would ultimately produce a very dense canopy that should help choke out the blackberry bushes, hawthorns, and reed canary grasses that had once dominated this stretch, and were sure to return in force once the road work was finished. Overplanting, as this pattern is sometimes called, also ensured that even with only a modest survival rate, the total number of trees remaining would produce a substantial canopy. This was an important part of the strategy because the restoration would not include a watering program. I studied the trees and reflected on their considerable size. I was pretty sure that without a good supply of water in the summer, most of them would die.

The target area was roughly a quarter of an acre and was cordoned off from the rest of the park by what appeared to be a recently installed silt fence. Holes had been dug twelve to fourteen feet apart and just deep enough to bury the ball up to the crown. These looked a little skimpy to me, especially in the diameter department. But I didn't happen to have a tape ruler with me and neither did any of the crew. Stout poles eight or ten feet in length lay nearby and would be used to support the trees once they were in the ground. In short, the process was pretty similar to what anyone planting a small tree or shrub might use in their own backyard, just scaled up to accommodate the needs of the larger diameter stock.

I watched for a while as Jesus skillfully rolled more trees towards their awaiting holes. The sweet, tangy aroma of evergreens hung thick in the cold air, reminding me that Christmas was less than a week away. What a great present for the watershed! The weather had improved a little, so I decided to take a quick loop through the park. I thanked the crew for their cooperation and headed south towards the place where Vermont Creek crosses under Oleson Road and enters the property. I decided to skirt the dense stands of blackberry south of the planting area by walking along the eastern boundary on the first stretch of sidewalk this park has ever seen.

The park was in for some great changes, and soon there would be a sign announcing the date of their arrival. In the November 2008 elections, Washington County voters passed a 100 million dollar bond measure aimed at helping THPRD preserve natural areas and upgrade and expand parks. The passage of this measure in a year when the local economy was crumbling speaks volumes about the importance to local residents of parks and recreation. It also says a lot about THPRD's reputation. A major portion of that bond is being used to pursue its natural resources agenda. The district currently manages around 1,300 acres of property, including some of the largest chunks of relatively undisturbed land remaining in the Fanno Creek watershed. Bauman is one of those properties and as such will finally be tended by professional crews on a sustained basis. The final draft of a master plan for the park's restoration project was in the process of being crafted even as I was crunching my way through the snow and frozen underbrush.[26] It's likely that the Fans of Fanno Creek will continue to contribute to the restoration and maintenance of the park as that plan is implemented; but from here on out THPRD will be doing the heavy lifting.

I walked to the northeast bank of the Fanno/Vermont confluence, usually an impossible place to reach but accessible now, thanks to the snow weighing on the blackberries that otherwise would have screened the view. It's a god-awfully sad and unnatural place really, especially when both streams run large as

26 THPRD (2009)

they were that day. Fanno is straightened for a hundred yards upstream, which gives it a chance to pick up a full head of steam before it slams into a heavily armored, vertical embankment that sends it downstream toward the head of the marsh at the Episcopal School. Pitiful little Vermont Creek, usually just a trickle but now a small torrent, came plowing into the main stem from the east. Where the two creeks merged the water boiled.

I turned north and began making my way up Fanno Creek towards the parking area and my truck. Before long I entered a thick patch of very young blackberry canes, most barely tall enough to have their heads out of the snow. This was an area, I knew, where the Fans had cut down every last cane and had even pulled most of their roots; but the blackberry was rapidly returning, as it invariably does the moment you stop beating it back. Better the blackberry than the English ivy I was thinking, just as a pair of wood ducks sped out of the woods and down the center of the creek to my left. What a magical sight and what a sweet promise. It was the third or fourth time in the last couple years that I had stirred up a pair of these fabulous birds along this particular reach. Maybe, come the spring, one of the larger trees in the central portion of the park would become home to a nest of them.

"Merry Christmas," I said out loud, as much to the creek as to myself.

Ric's place on a part of Fanno Creek floodplain

3—The Accidental Advocate

Deer Hunting

A pair of mallards blasted out of the reeds to my right, so close they seemed to come up from behind. Across the wetlands they sped, low on the water until they reached the embankment at the end, where they banked steeply to the left and vanished behind a dense stand of small trees. I had time to raise the telephoto, point it in their general direction, and take one shot before they were gone. There was nothing in the replayed image but the blurred tops of the distant tree line. Had my lens been a .12 gauge I still would have missed them by a mile. I'd entered their zone as carefully as possible, intent on trying to creep up on a deer I was certain could not be more than a few yards ahead of me. However effective my stealthy creeping may have been, my cover had been blown. By now the deer would be long gone.

I first spotted the doe from the road as I swept the area with my telephoto before actually entering the property. She stepped out of a thicket near the wetlands, as cool and calm as could be. She casually surveyed the area, then ambled off towards the scrub brush to the north. As soon as she was out of sight I snuck away from my vantage point and began the long, but ultimately fruitless stalk. Now I rose out of my crouched stance, happy to relax after the tension of the stalk. As the crow flies I was only about a hundred yards from where I had entered the property. To get here, however, I had been forced to work my way around, and ultimately through, the impenetrable thicket of blackberry that cuts across the front quarter of Ric's four-acre property.

I looked at my watch, unsurprised to see that I'd been at it for the better part of half an hour. The distance covered had been short, but the trek here had been challenging, particularly since I was trying to be as quiet as possible. By now the spooked deer was probably a mile away so I moved on more rapidly. The sun had cleared the hilltops and warehouses on the eastern horizon. The low-angled April light rushed through the few clouds remaining in the east and flooded the landscape to the west with a golden glow. The frost that had covered everything when I arrived that morning had vanished. Last year's vegetation, flattened by wind, rain and floodwaters, lay in knee-high piles of blonde brush that crowded the flanks of the wetlands. Deep green spikes, probably the new shoots of reed canary grass, poked up everywhere among the litter. They signaled the start of the next onslaught of this lovely but tyrannical invasive.

As I moved out of the marsh and closer to Fanno Creek, the grass gave way to dense thickets of willow and hawthorn, which in their turn gave way to stands of ash and occasional Douglas firs. Where the pathway passed through the margin between thickets and wetlands I found a good-sized pile of steaming deer scat. "That close, damn it," I muttered to myself. A moment later I stepped out of the thicket and onto the banks of Fanno Creek.

That day in April I had been creek-crawling for less than a year. I was only beginning to get my head around the geography and physics of the system. I knew, for example, that I was just a third of a mile downstream from where Ball Creek, one of the most hammered tributaries in the system, joins the main stem. I also knew that I was just over a mile from the heart of downtown Tigard and less than two miles from Fanno Creek's confluence with the Tualatin River. I figured I was standing about 100 feet outside the west boundary of the property I'd come to reconnoiter, and that this put me just inside the boundaries of a sizeable area belonging to the city of Tigard. But where the finer points of Fanno Creek's complex systems were concerned my knowledge base was still slim, a fact I tried to stress with the owner of this property at our first meeting. "Ric, I know just enough about this watershed stuff to be really dangerous," I told him.

He laughed good naturedly and said he was surprised to hear it. "You were highly recommended as someone who might be able to fully appreciate the potential of my idea. I'm counting on you to give me an unbiased view of what I have on this property in the way of natural resources. That sort of information might have an impact on whether I go forward with my project. That could have a big impact on how I grow my business. So I guess you could say my future is in your hands."

We both laughed at that, but it made me nervous all the same. I promised him some good pictures and honest feedback, but again stressed the limits of my knowledge and influence where land development activities in the watershed were concerned. My perspective would come free of charge, I told him, but that was the best thing I could say about it.

Ric's "project" involved building of a new warehouse for his commercial painting business. He already owned the property, a four-acre piece of bottom land located on a reach of Fanno Creek that is of particular concern to anyone who wants to preserve the watershed's remaining wetlands as much as possible. It's one of the largest reasonably intact floodplains on the creek. Prior to Tigard's incorporation in 1961, the area was used mostly for farming and a little light industry. Railways, including the Oregon Electric trolley system came to the uplands on the east side of the creek in 1907, which helped connect farmers and other commercial interests with the major markets in other parts of the state and throughout the Northwest. Industrial and commercial development in this area has been focused mostly on the eastern side of the creek, while residential growth has been most pronounced along its western uplands. The growth on both sides of the creek has been marked in the last few decades; in most cases that development has come right up to the edge of the floodplain—in some cases, even right up to the edge of the stream. What remained undeveloped, at least for the time being, were bottom lands that are deep, rough and relatively undisturbed.

Jolly Roger's Cow

I studied the rain-swollen surface of Fanno creek for a while longer, wondering how often Ric actually made it out to this part of his property. What a great place to study the amazing things taking place on the opaque surface—like the deep gash I could see forming along the waterline on the opposite side of the stream. "Scour," the Watershed Folk generally call the fierce cutting action. Where the creek rubs up against the bottom and the sides of the channel, its volume, speed, and load of silt and debris would shear off massive amounts of gravel, sediment and vegetation. The dislodged materials would load the water with fresh tools for its work on the next vulnerable downstream area. The faster moving parts of the flow would carry good-sized gravels that would hammer and chisel at any materials they ran into, other rocks included. Smaller particles would abrade mud and rock alike.

And all the while the creek was scouring out the channel, it would not only be trying to get downstream, it would also be trying to break out of the bed itself. I picked up a section of fallen tree limb perhaps maybe two inches in diameter, gripped it hard in anticipation of the stream's reaction, and stuck it into the flow. It snapped like a twig. The remnant went spinning out of sight around the bend in seconds.

For a while I was lost in the sounds of the water and the warmth of the sun. For no particular reason, my attention turned toward a portion of the bank on the other side of the creek—just in time to see it give way. A clump of dirt about the size of a wheelbarrow slid almost silently into the water. For a second or two a darker shade of brown prevailed on the surface of the flow until its comet-like structure completely vanished. I didn't pretend to comprehend the dynamics of the main body of the flow—that portion of the stream that never touches banks or bottoms—but its speedy handling of the dirt showed that mysterious things were going on inside that swirling greenish-brown mass of busy water.

I continued upstream until a tangle of brush and fallen hawthorn trees too deep to tackle without gloves and a chain saw blocked my progress. The path of least resistance led away from the creek and deeper into the underbrush. I made progress for a few minutes, then suddenly found myself blocked in every direction, except backwards. Just a few yards in front of me the bright green of a grassy clearing was framed by a jungle of ivy-covered ash trees marking the nearest meander of the creek. I pressed ahead, making a hell of a racket in the process, and burst through the brush and out onto the bank just in time to see a Herford heifer making a mad scramble up the opposite bank.

By the time I had untangled my camera and pulled off a shot she was well out into the pasture. She turned toward me briefly, lowed resentfully and plodded towards a small herd of cows grazing in the north end of the pasture. I hadn't expected to see livestock so near to downtown Tigard, much less directly on the creek. On one hand their presence made sense, given the recent agricultural nature of the area. But something about it struck me as odd and wrong. Later in the morning the implications of this chance encounter would become clear to me, but now I was too preoccupied with Ric's project and its environmental challenges to spend much time thinking about cows and creeks.

Ric's Dilemma

I hunkered down on the bank, broke open a pack of peanut butter crackers, and pulled the thermos of coffee out of my backpack. While I munched and slurped on one of the best field breakfasts around, I studied the creek as it skirted the edges of the pastureland and flowed away to the south. The stream bank to the north was heavily incised and too steep for cattle to make it in and out of the creek. But across from where I was eating breakfast the bank was rounded off and showed signs of heavy wear. Further to my left, just before the creek vanished around a tight corner, the embankment was even more gently sloped. The startled cow had exited the stream there before stopping on the top of the bank to look me over. What a beating this poor creek has taken from farmers over the years, I thought. And pretty much everyone else, as well. We humans and our animals can mess up an ecosystem faster than practically any other force on the planet.

This line of thinking led me back to the task at hand. It is not often—or at least, not often enough—that small business owners go out of their way to engage in dialogues with the local environmental community about how best to develop commercial property. That's particularly true where development near or in so-called "sensitive lands" is concerned. But Ric had moved in that direction when he realized that obtaining building permits for a new warehouse on his property was going to be prohibitively expensive. The problem was fundamental—all but a small portion of his property lay well within the floodplain and, in most cases, within a flourishing wetland. The upland portion of his property, the only suitable land for a structure, was crowded into the northeast corner of the lot, and even a large portion of this space consisted of fill. There was simply no place on the property large enough to legally build a large warehouse and its attendant parking and docking areas.

At one time Ric might have been able to resolve his dilemma without much fuss and extra expense. The building might have been erected on pilings driven into the soft muck of the floodplain, or more fill dirt might have been trucked in to create a longer and wider shelf across the front of the property. But over the last fifty years multiple factors have combined to make such practices mostly a thing of the past. The Clean Water Act of 1972 was one of these factors, as were the development of a regional governmental structure in 1979 and the reorganization of Clean Water Services in the late 1990s. Each of these events led to new benchmarks for health and safety concerns and attendant watershed management practices. Perhaps the greatest factor, however, was an ever-growing understanding among engineers of the way wetlands and floodplains function in relation to flood events and their control. Combined, these factors have led to the development of state, regional and municipal approaches to land use issues that are significantly more informed and holistic than ever before. But while it is much more difficult to obtain building permits where sensitive lands are involved in a project, it is not always impossible, thanks to a process called "wetlands mitigation."

The wetlands mitigation process is conducted under the administration of the Oregon Department of State Lands (DSL) and governed under Oregon's Removal-Fill Law of 1967 and the Wetlands Conservation Act of 1989. In essence the process requires a prospective builder to avoid, reduce, or compensate for damage that may be done to the wetlands during an excavation or fill-work project. The size, shape and location of the footprint for the projected warehouse was not the only factor Ric would have to consider in this process, nor was the DSL the only permitting authority that would be involved. By the time Ric and his architect had taken the various challenges into consideration, there was simply no way that the development could take place without significantly impacting the sensitive lands involved. Moving the project forward would require some level of compensatory mitigation, which is to say that Ric's project had become an even more expensive proposition.

There are four basic ways in which a developer may mitigate against unavoidable damages to a wetland: onsite mitigation, which is usually the easiest and best approach; off-site mitigation, which involves effecting the mitigation at some other appropriate site; the purchase of mitigation credits from a mitigation bank, an option when on-site mitigation is not practicable or environmentally preferable; and "payment to provide mitigation," meaning a direct payment to DSL in proportion to the lost environmental services. Initially, Ric hoped he might be able to get by with onsite mitigation; but when his property was inspected, he learned there was simply not enough undeveloped land involved to make onsite mitigation possible. After further study he learned that the probable cost of offsite mitigation would almost certainly be prohibitive. That was when he decided to reach out to the environmental community. Perhaps they might be interested in picking up some, or even the entire portion, of the mitigation load.

A small stand of ash trees probably killed by repeated flooding in the area

With the help of his architect, Ric had managed to contact a few of the more well-placed individuals in the watershed, one of whom sent the particulars of the proposal along to me. "You should look at this place, if you can," the contact had told me, "because your book will be incomplete without mention of it. It's part of an extremely important stretch of the creek. Someday, with any luck at all, it could be part of Metro's Regional Trail System. Much of the property in that corridor is prime habitat, some of the very best left in the entire Fanno Creek system."

I demurred at first because I was still little more than an aspiring student of wetlands issues. But curiosity about the place finally overcame my reservations. One pass through the area a few days later convinced me that my friend was right. Still, I was deeply concerned that Ric might get the impression that I was actually "somebody," or that I might be able to pull strings or otherwise help resolve the regulatory side of his issue.

I met Ric at his office, which is crammed into a tiny old farmhouse perched on the highest point of the property, a triangular area on the northeast corner of the lot. He was a youngish-looking, animated guy and I liked him right off. One of the first things he said was, "Painting has been very good to me." He noted my quick glance around the crowded and eclectically furnished office and grinned. "Ok, ok, so it hasn't made me rich, I'll admit; but it's a good living, and the business has been steadily growing for over ten years. That's why I need this warehouse, so I can take my business up the next step on the ladder." He chuckled over his pun, then explained the basic dimensions of the problem: too little usable acreage, too many building restrictions and not enough cash on hand to afford an offsite fix. In the early days he had been able to cram most of his gear and supplies into the farmhouse, but for a couple years now, he had been forced to house it in temporary sheds, containers, and plastic-covered pallets around the high ground of the property.

Ric spread the architect's plans on the table and pointed to the corner of the building where he planned to place his new office. "That's the southwestern exposure and looks out over an old oxbow where the creek used to flow. There's a little marsh there now. I want to be able to look out of my office and watch the ducks, heron, deer and all the other game that lives out there."

Ric had grown up in Dayton, a small farming community twenty miles away, and had spent much of his earlier life "fooling around on the Yamhill River." The experience had shaped him in many ways, and he was eager to recapture a sense of that connection to the outdoors. That had been one of the main attractions of the property, he said. "That, and it was real cheap," he laughed. "Up until the last couple of years we had been pretty self-contained; but the curse of succeeding in business is that you have to keep growing. This place was barely big enough to start with, and if I can't work out a way to build this warehouse

I'm going to have to bite the bullet and look for some off-site storage, or even a new piece of land. That could get very expensive."

Yes, the property must have been "affordable," and for good reason, I thought to myself as I rose from the bank and dusted cracker crumbs off the front of my jacket. By the time I moved through the woods and reentered Ric's property at the northeast corner I had decided that the acreage was almost completely useless as a commercial site, maybe even more useless than Ric himself might be prepared to admit. My convictions about the property's low commercial value grew as I moved into a stand of tall ash trees standing in a mud-filled swale. Half of them were obviously dead, but the branches of the rest were in full bud. Before one of the trees had died a beaver had girdled it, leaving a core about six inches in diameter. Later the dead remnant had been toppled, knocked down by the wind, I guessed, since it had fallen with its head upstream. It had happened several years ago, I concluded after studying the gray, moss-covered carcass. Virtually all of the dead trees were of similar size, approximately 24 to 32 inches in circumference and around forty feet tall. What had happened here, I wondered? If these trees had drowned, why hadn't the rest, particularly those at a deeper level in the swale? Could they have been poisoned by some toxic artifact left over from one of the farms or small industries that used to lie upstream from here? But, again, why had only some of the trees succumbed? There seemed no pattern to the business, so I let it go and moved on.

My mental and physical meanderings had taken me to the north property line. There was an old, burnt-out electric fence along that side. I walked beside it for a while, then headed south again, back towards the place where I had jumped the ducks. As I walked up to the wetlands, a small nutria slithered through a grassy hole in the reeds lining the pool and slid down the bank. Seconds later it crawled out on a muddy ledge along the opposite shore before turning a hairy eyeball in my direction. "You brazen bastard!" I exclaimed. "If I had a gun, I'd shoot you myself." Reacting to the sound of my voice, or maybe to the menace in it, the creature plunged into the muddy water and vanished beneath the surface. I could tell the direction of its flight because the water was shallow and his bow wake made a recurrent pattern of V shaped ripples that pointed like an animated arrow towards the far end of the pond. I watched until the surface stopped undulating, hoping to get another photograph. The nutria never reappeared, so I headed for the truck. It had been a thought-provoking outing and I needed to record my mental impressions before they vanished like the ripples on the pond.

Budweiser Boulevard

I opened the door to Starbucks and was enveloped in the aroma I've learned to love so well. Creek crawling usually heightens my senses and observational abilities, but it doesn't take long for what I've absorbed to dissipate into a cloud of fuzzy recollections. To combat this, the minute I crawl out of the creek I beat feet to the nearest coffee shop for a little download time. I took my latte and butter croissant to a small table next to the windows, pulled my laptop out of its case, and went to work making a quick list of things that had been bumping around in my brain since I'd left Ric's place.

The first thing to deal with was Ric's dilemma. I decided that it was a fairly straightforward problem. His land would not support the building of a 10,000-square-foot warehouse and construction of the attendant parking lots and so on. He'd need at least an acre or more of land well out of the floodplain to do that, and right now the best he could muster was a small triangle of upland on the northeast corner of the lot. The formula for onsite enhancements was something like two acres of enhancements for every acre lost through development. Ric's lot was just four acres. If he could build out at all, the probable cost of mitigation would be substantial, easily into the tens, and maybe even into the hundreds, of thousands of dollars. In the end it might be less expensive, not to mention a lot easier, to simply move his business. However, if he decided to bite the bullet and build onsite, I wasn't sure he could count on a lot of interest and help from the environmental community. His place was covered in nothing but invasive plants. Any effort to restore it to something close to a natural area would cost a bundle and take a long time.

One way or the other it was Ric's dilemma, not mine, and I had to keep that in mind at all times. I'd told Ric that I wasn't a consultant and that my main interest in his project was the impact it might have on the general health of Fanno Creek. In a day or two I would give him some pictures, some general information and some free advice. ("It's as good as every dime you've paid for it, Ric," I would say.) Then I'd have to butt out. I had neither the skills nor the time necessary to help him. I wasn't kidding when I told him that my level of knowledge about the processes he was dealing with probably made me more dangerous than useful.

The walk through Ric's wetlands had given me a much better sense of the entire stretch of Fanno Creek between Bonita and Durham Road. It appeared to have great potential as a natural area, but it was obviously more ignored than loved by the property owners on either of its banks. Most of the acreage was private property, a major problem so far as its overall potential as a natural area might be concerned. As with most of the other significant wetlands areas in Tigard, the ecological value of this mile-long strip of land was well understood by the public agencies and not-for-profit advocacy groups involved with the affairs of Fanno Creek. But while it was on their radar, I had the growing impression that it was nowhere near the center of the screen. It was "protected" to some extent, but only by virtue of the fact that it could not be developed easily or inexpensively.

I thought back to the barren, hoof-scarred bank on the west side of the creek and the small herd of cattle that had done the damage. It was early April and the recent rains had the creek running high and fast enough to create small whirlpools that played on the surface as the water sped past my vantage point. Those cattle were probably content to drink from the bank for now; but I was sure that summer would find them up to their shanks in the creek.

Ric's dilemma had developed from constraints imposed by multiple regulatory agencies operating at the state, regional and municipal level. How were these agencies disposed towards agricultural activities such as the one taking place just across the creek from Ric's property? As I ground away at the encounter, I realized that I was very upset about that cow, almost as irritated as when I'd jumped the nutria. Why the burn, I wondered? It was just a small herd, not a damn feedlot. Get over it, I told myself.

Something else was nagging at me as well. It had to do with my book project. I was making progress on all fronts and had found the Watershed Folk to be accessible and supportive. But something about the whole thing had somehow changed; not with the basic structure of the book so much as with where the research was beginning to take me. It didn't seem to matter if I was looking through documents and books in my study or stumbling around in the urban bush, peering through branches at the creek; I kept running into things that brought me up short and made me ask "What the hell...?" Like that damn cow.

I decided to drive by the upper end of the pasture on my way home. It was only a couple miles away. Maybe—if the situation seemed right—I could introduce myself to anyone around and see what else I could learn about the property. On the way I rehearsed different versions of my greeting and introduction. I was still struggling with exactly what I might say to the owner of the acreage as I left the main thoroughfare and headed up the narrow street towards the north end of the pasture. It was an odd little deadend street, posted all over with "no parking" and "no turn-around" signs that didn't look as if they'd been made by a municipal authority. It came to an end more abruptly than I had anticipated. The map I was carrying showed the street as being almost a mile long, but in less than 1000 feet I came to a dead end in the form of a wire fence stretched across the road. A sign on the fence said "No Tresspassing (sic)." A dirt road leading off to the left was signed "Do Not Enter." A road sign on a metal pole next to the turnoff said "Budweiser Boulevard." To the right a gravel road led uphill to a small house perched on a little rise. Above the roof waved a black flag sporting a crudely rendered skull-and-crossbones. Any thought of making direct contact with the local folk quickly left my mind. I carefully backed out of the area, all the way down to the main cross street then headed for home. I wasn't sure what to do next, but I knew that Brian Wegner at TRK might be able to help me with next-steps.

Rat Bastard

"Yeah, we're familiar with that property," said Brian. "Give me a copy of the picture and I'll forward it to the ODA."

I goggled at him. The District Attorney? Wasn't that going a bit overboard, I asked? "I mean, it was only a cow, not a crime scene."

He grimaced and shook his head. "I mean the Department of Agriculture. They're the ones who deal with these kinds of situations. You should fill out a complaint yourself. It helps if the complaint comes from several different sources."

I demurred. "I don't even know these folks."

"That doesn't matter. This is not a personal thing. It's about doing what's right for the creek and the folks downstream. These people aren't likely to get into serious trouble anyway, unless they're already on notice for earlier infractions. The ODA has a full plate and doesn't usually resort to punitive measures unless there's some serious badness going on." He went on to explain that most agencies in the state try to find win-win solutions to these kinds of problems. In general that meant helping the landowners better understand how their actions might be damaging the environment, then helping them make changes in their operations that would do a better job of protecting it.

"Sounds awfully Republican to me," I said, "you know, a little *laissez faire*?"

He laughed and then got serious again. "Look, crazy things go on in these wetlands all the time, and no one can get to all of them. You have to pick your battles. That's true at every level of government, and it's especially true in the advocacy business."

"I don't think I want to be in the advocacy business," I objected.

"Too late now. Your watershed is counting on you," he laughed. "We'll report this to the ODA, they'll work through a process with the land owner, and that will be that. Chances are it will be effective, at least for the short term." He messed with his keyboard a minute. "I've sent you the link to the form you'll need when you file your complaint with the agency," he said. "Now go home and do your duty."

Later in the evening I pulled up the form[27] and studied it for a while. I was a little surprised at how conflicted I felt. Maybe if I had walked up to Jolly Roger's front door and looked someone directly in the face, I might have had a better sense of where I stood. . But just filling out a form and essentially ratting

---

27 Blank forms may be obtained online at http://www.oregon.gov/ODA/NRD/docs/pdf/water/wq_complaint_form.pdf

on a total stranger made me a little uneasy. On the other hand, I couldn't just turn a blind eye to the situation, particularly after I had gone online and visited the ODA site. The property was clearly in violation of water quality regulations and Fanno Creek was taking the hit. I did my best Tevye impression for the next half hour, going back and forth from one side of the argument to the other until I had exhausted all of the "on the other hands" I could think of. In the end I filled it out and mailed it; but I didn't feel good about it.

I could have saved myself a lot of soul searching, as well as any further direct involvement in the situation, had I known that my picture of the cow had already been circulated to other environmental interests. Even before I sealed the flap on an envelope, the photo and two other formal complaints against the property had been routed to the Department of Agriculture.

A couple days later I received an email from one of the department's field agents. "As one of the complainants..." it began. I felt my shoulders tighten. The note, which merely confirmed receipt of the complaint and indicated some dates scheduled for the follow-up site visit, gave me an opportunity to talk directly to a representative of the department, so I made the call. From the outset the agent echoed most of Brian's basic remarks: the department works proactively in these kinds of situations and she did not anticipate anything like real friction or hostility from the landowners. She also provided a clear outline of the process the agency uses when it follows up on a complaint.

First, the owner is notified that there's been a complaint and a site visit is scheduled. If the alleged violation is not observed at the time of this visit, then the owner receives a letter of compliance and the case is closed. If a violation isn't observed at the time, but the potential exists for one in the future, a Water Quality Advisory is issued. In many cases the Advisory comes with helpful recommendations and maybe even a scheduled follow-up visit. If the site visit turns up a clear violation of Oregon Administrative Standards, a Letter of Warning is issued. This comes with recommendations as well as compliance criteria and a date is scheduled for an inspection. At this point there is considerable pressure on the landowner to comply, but there is also a great deal of assistance available, some of which can be financial.

The Department's end goal is compliance, not coercion; every effort is made to help the violator fix the situation. As a result, several Warnings may be issued before more punitive measures are taken. This is particularly the case when a landowner is making a legitimate effort to develop a strategy that will result in compliance. Other organizations may also provide the landowner with assistance as s/he works towards compliance, most notably the local Soil and Water Conservation District or the Natural Resources Conservation Service.

This sounded like a pretty lenient approach to the enforcement of state regulatory policy. You usually don't encounter these kinds of soft hands when you deal with other public agencies. But the department's representative pointed out that the enforcement procedures related to these kinds of water quality issues are as pragmatic as they are fair. Farmers and ranchers work in an environment usually dominated by the elements. Storms can blow down traditional fences or interrupt service to electrical ones, something the owner can't be expected to control. Where wetlands are concerned, weather-related events, particularly flooding , can destroy barricades, inundate areas where manure or other agricultural byproducts have been stored, even change the lay of the land itself. In the end, the agency is less interested in culpability than it is in correction; so it takes a constructive, even collaborative, approach to situations such as the one I'd stumbled into when I walked Ric's property.

This information put my mind a little more at ease about my role in the process. So, what happens next, I wanted to know? The ODA agent explained that we were already at step two. The property had been in violation before, largely for the same issues. The owners claimed that recent heavy rains had led to flooding over some of the property, and a pile of stream-driven debris had ripped out a large section of the electric fence controlling the cattle's access to the stream. Fortunately, they were being very cooperative and seemed generally open to finding a permanent solution. Bottom line, she felt the agency could work with these people to develop a plan and find the resources they needed to fix the problem. "Check back later if you'd like to know what kind of progress we end up making with this one," she suggested. I could tell from her tone that she was comfortable with the situation and optimistic about its outcome, so I decided to feel likewise.

Within a week the incident had vanished from my radar. But while I was able to put the episode behind me, I could not ignore the fact that as a researcher I had crossed an important line. I had become a "complainant," an individual with an issue. An activist, maybe even a "goddamned Snail Darter Environmentalist,[28]" God forbid. I shuddered at the thought. At the outset of my endeavor I had made the words "know your watershed" my mantra. I was going to be all eyes and ears, all existential encounter, and at the same time somehow duck the attendant recoil. More than anything else I wanted to remain uninvolved in any of the issues I stumbled across. Even when I decided that there might be material for a book in the enterprise, I was determined to remain above the fray. I figured I could be informed, insightful—even critical— without actually getting involved. People do it all the time. But at some point in my walk across Ric's property, I had been transformed from a mere visitor to the watershed into one of its inhabitants. Things between me and the creek would never be the same.

28 BgPapa (2009)

Great Blue Heron on Fanno Creek

4—The Wild Side

Life on the Edge[29]

From the mud in its streambeds to the treetops in its uplands, Fanno Creek teems with wildlife. Beat up as it is, there's still a lot of habitat available for anything that can adapt to it. Crappy habitat, for the most part, but habitat nonetheless. About half of the Fanno Creek watershed is covered with non-organic material. This shell of concrete and other building materials is distributed more or less uniformly, except where narrow bands of vegetation, a few of them quite long, thread themselves through neighborhoods and along highway corridors. There are trees scattered almost everywhere throughout the watershed, but rarely do they appear in stands. A few are quite old, such as the big cottonwood in front of the Fanno Farmhouse, but the majority of the established trees around here are less than a hundred years old. [30] From an environmental standpoint, we live in a highly degraded area that in most ways is very much like every other heavily urbanized area in America. Except that ours is a little younger.

Urbanization did not come to this part of the Pacific Northwest until very late in the nineteenth century, so development hasn't had time to completely degrade the environment to the same extent as it has in older, more well-established cities. For example, population density for Beaverton stands at 4,664 persons per square mile, whereas Seattle stands at 7,136. (Los Angeles, just by way of comparison, stands at 8,205. The density in Manhattan is a whopping 71,201.) We Northwesterners haven't been here all that long, either. Beaverton incorporated in 1893, Seattle in 1869. By comparison, Los Angeles was founded in 1781. Manhattan can date its lineage back to 1625, almost 390 years ago. Expansion over time = rate of urbanization, it's as simple as that.

I mention all this because sometimes I'll be in a public meeting, a city planning session for example, and I detect a bit of "green" smugness. Whenever I hear PR pronouncements about how "livable" the region is, or how it ranks "high in environmental awareness," I get a little uncomfortable. For one thing, I'm never too sure what these phrases actually *mean*, particularly when they're used by politicians or real estate organizations. "Livability" is such a fuzzy and relativistic term that it must have been coined by an ad man. And what exactly does it mean to be environmentally aware, especially these days, when any real distinction between the terms "conservationism" and "environmentalism" has become almost non-existent, as far as common usage is concerned?

I never hear these immodest pronouncements from Watershed Folk because they know how critical the environmental situation is here in the Tualatin Basin.

29 Wilson (2000)
30 The cottonwood is approximately 150 years old.

They know that someday vast tracts of farmland in the western portions of the valley may disappear under waves of concrete and glass. They also know that it could happen even more rapidly than it did in the mid-1800s, when the oak savannahs once filling that vastness disappeared beneath the plow. They also recognize that the green infrastructure currently supporting the biotic health of Fanno Creek is so minimal, and in such desperate condition, that the watershed lies at a tipping point. As one of them once put it to me, "When it's gone it's gone. And, Eric, it is going, going...."

One of the key indicators of a watershed's general health is the condition and the behaviors of its biota. Lori Hennings, a Senior Natural Resources Scientist for Metro, has her fingers on that pulse. Her work focuses on water, land and air quality issues, particularly those that may negatively impact the utility of each as a resource for the community. When I first met her, she was working on a project aimed at defining wildlife corridors throughout the Metro Regional Boundary. At that point she had developed a GIS map showing some of the actual habitat linkages still intact within the region. The map could be read three ways, one showing where corridors still existed; another showing where and how corridors had been lost; and a third showing, by inference, corridors that might be retrieved through land acquisitions and other means.

She used Sylvan Creek, one of my favorite tributaries, as an example. "See here?" she said, tapping on the monitor. "The uppermost reaches of your creek flow out of this area above the intersection of Highway 26 and Canyon Road. You can tell from the map that it's heavily overgrown, and if we drilled down to the roadways level"—click, click with the mouse—"we would see that the road cuts directly across its middle and creates a gauntlet for any north-south movement of critters between the upper sections and downstream sections to the south. Bigger game, I mean. This culvert on the north side of 26 actually serves as a highway to the south for many of the smaller species, so in some ways we have continuity between the upper and middle reaches of Sylvan Creek, and in others we don't."

What a great project! I told her so. Her smile was quickly followed by a slight frown. "Yes, I am very excited about it; but right now there's no field work budgeted for it, so I'm not sure when I'll be able to really focus any more time on the project. Too bad. Connectivity, or rather the lack of connectivity, is one of our urban wildlife's greatest challenges."

The conversation shifted to my book and my field research, and I told her the story about Brad and the invasive oak he'd cut down in Bauman Park. I confessed that for a long time I was troubled by the notion of cutting down something living and obviously in prime condition. Halfway through my narrative Lori snorted and began shaking her head. "Get over it," she gently scolded me, "Look, it's all about how these non-natives don't fit in at the systemic level. Here's just one example out of a dozen: When birds are raising their young they need insects, many times a specific species or a group of specific species. Birds go for the bugs because they need the protein. The insects need specific species of plants because of the relative life-cycles involved as much as for the food groups. If it had been allowed to grow to maturity, that non-native oak might produce the right kind of food for the bugs, but not at the right time. Bye-bye birdies, hello infestations of bugs we might not want to see in such overabundance."

I pressed Lori for more examples of challenges to urban wildlife. The loss or degradation of habitat, connectivity and invasive species are all serious challenges, she told me; but perhaps the most difficult issue to manage effectively was the interaction between people and the wild animals that are increasingly forced to live within the human community. Conflicts between humans and animals in urbanized areas are a growing concern to governments and environmental groups everywhere.

"Have you ever heard of Stan Gehrt and the Cook County Urban Coyote Project?" she asked. "He was the keynote speaker at the last symposium. You should study that project."

Houdini's Hound

The Urban Ecosystem Research Consortium (UERC) is one of the fastest-growing, ecologically grounded partnerships in the Pacific Northwest. Comprised of individuals from a wide range of non-profit organizations who represent an even wider range of scientific, educational and governmental backgrounds, the consortium focuses on "...advancing the science of urban ecosystems and (improving) our understanding of them."[31] Partly to that end UERC annually presents a day-long symposium devoted to the presentation of recent ecosystem research conducted in the Portland/Vancouver metropolitan region. Presenters run the gamut from grad students to watershed project managers. I attended the 2008 presentation and came away feeling as if I had been on an informational binge. I ingested so much new information, and was bombarded with so many fresh concepts, that the next day I had the intellectual equivalent of a hangover. I've been back to every symposium since then, and each time I come away more informed and more motivated than ever.

Part of the appeal of the symposia is that all presentations but the keynote addresses are held to a ten minute limit. If the presenter hasn't wrapped everything up in that time, one of the consortium members sitting up front starts raising hell on a duck call. It's as effective as it is funny. This means that you end up hearing a somewhat expanded abstract of each of the projects. It also

31 UERC (2012)

means that in a single day you can get a pretty good overview of some of the most recent research in the area. The proceedings include a catalogue of that research, complete with citation and contact information for the presenters, which provides attendees ample opportunity to pursue specific studies if they choose. Given our increasing propensity for living off byte-sized information, this kind of presentation is extremely user friendly.

Stan Gehrt was the keynote speaker for the 2008 afternoon sessions. His presentation was titled *Unraveling the Mysteries of Urban Wildlife: The Next Frontier for Conservation*. Gehrt is an engaging speaker, which sometimes upstages the fact that he is also border-line brilliant. His study of coyote behaviors in the Chicago area has revolutionized the field of wildlife research by establishing a better understanding of how urban areas are becoming the New Wilderness. Gehrt and his colleagues have captured and tagged more than 200 coyotes in the greater Chicago area. They estimate that anywhere from several hundred to a few thousand of the animals may be living in and around the city at any given time. Some of these coyotes live in city parks and semi-abandoned inter-urban areas, but many more live along the margins of apartment complexes, golf courses, commercial buildings and industrial areas.[32]

As urbanization continues to spread deeper into what were once rural and wilderness areas, the old frontier begins to shrink and the new one continues to expand. If you are a wildlife biologist these days," he's fond of pointing out, "you are an *urban* wildlife biologist whether you like it or not. There's simply no way around it."

I'm not sure if anyone has a good idea of how many coyotes live within Metro's regional boundary at any one moment. Thousands, no doubt, but how many thousands would be useful information. In his presentation Gehrt pointed to many aspects of coyote behavior that both wildlife managers and citizens need to keep in mind at all times. The coyote is one of the most highly adaptable predators on the planet. It is a very fast learner, second among urban animals only to the human, the raccoon and maybe the starling. It can meet rapid changes in the environment by adjusting not only the shape, location and size of its range, but by altering its reproduction rates as well.[33] Its adaptability is exceeded only by its uncanny elusiveness. Finally, it is a consummate escape artist. Gehrt cracked all of us up with stories about his attempts to photograph coyotes stealing eggs from the nests of Canada geese. All but one of the photos he presented showed little more than a blurred body part sticking into the frame.

Although Gehrt's presentation was entertaining, the details he provided of the coyote's ranging ability were sobering. A pack that he and his colleagues

32 Ohio State (2005)
33 Faced with reductions of food resources, the coyote lowers its rate of reproduction; but it responds to increased predation by increasing it reproductions rates.

had been studying for more than three years had a range that included the northern end of O'Hare Airport. I'm not sure what impressed me most about this pack of coyotes, its choice of habitat or the fact that it was thriving in what seemed like a highly improbable place.

But there's a downside to the coyote's tremendous adaptability, particularly where lack of predation on the species is a condition. I camp in southeast Oregon frequently and, whether afoot or in my car, I've never been able to get much closer than 400 yards to a coyote. Like many other animals in that part of the country, they seem to understand that 400 yards is about the limit of accuracy for a rancher's 30.06. And even at that distance, the instant I raise my camera, they are gone. Most urban coyotes used to be similarly gun-shy, but more and more of them have learned that showing up in someone's backyard or on a playground in broad daylight isn't usually going to get them shot. Given that coyotes learn so well and so fast, it isn't surprising to find that increasing numbers of them are becoming almost as unafraid of their human neighbors as the squirrels tend to be.

The coyote's increasingly marked and sometimes threatening presence in areas it once avoided may ultimately force communities in this area to consider actions similar to those taken in Sherwood, a city just sixteen miles from downtown Portland. In late September of 2008, the Sherwood police chief ordered officers to shoot coyotes on sight. This drastic measure was deemed necessary after multiple close encounters between humans and local coyotes, culminating in an incident in which a 15-year-old high school student was chased home by two coyotes that were clearly unafraid of him. Local environmental and wildlife groups initially condemned the decision out of hand. "Draconian," said some; "classic overreaction" said others.[34]

At the time I tended to agree, especially since the coyote has way more to fear from us than vice versa. But not long afterward, a young woman in Nova Scotia[35] was killed by a pack of coyotes, the first fully documented case of such a fatality. The coyotes involved were an eastern variety that has interbred with wolves and sometimes exhibits pack behaviors, which is uncommon among other varieties of coyote. I'd heard the story when it hit the news, but Nova Scotia is a long way away, so I didn't think that much about it. Then, one night, my youngest daughter was approached by a coyote in a manner that has had me rethinking the situation ever since.

At the time of the incident, my daughter, her husband and their two-year-old daughter lived in the small, rural town of Tenino, fifteen miles south of Olympia, Washington. She had come home from the grocery store alone after dark,

34 Manzano (2008); Salinger (2008)
35 Her name was Taylor Mitchell and the attack is detailed on one of the links of the Cook County, Illinois, Coyote Project website.

only to find the front porch light off and the door locked. She assumed that her husband was upstairs bathing the baby and began fumbling in her purse for the key. Suddenly she sensed that she was being watched. She turned away from the front door and found herself looking into the eyes of a coyote standing at the edge of the porch, not ten feet away. The coyote glowered at her a moment, dropped its head an inch or two, then growled and took a step forward.

Her instinctive response was a good one. She let out a loud yell and simultaneously threw her purse and the groceries at the coyote. The creature darted away into the shadows surrounding the porch. What haunted her most when she was finally inside and began to settle down was the fact for a couple of days just before the incident she had seen several coyotes, a family no doubt, trekking back and forth through the side yard in broad daylight. They had been passing through her daughter's play area. The realization made her blood run cold. From that day on she could not take the child out to play without being on edge the entire time.

Incidents of aggressive coyote behavior, including attacks on humans that draw blood, remain rare. Oregon's last reported coyote attack took place in June of 2012, when a five year old girl was attacked while playing on the sand dunes at Nehalem Beach.[36] So far, these kinds of events have been relatively isolated, and the details of the reports are frequently inaccurate or inflated. But one way or the other they are not good news for anyone who respects the coyote and its place in the scheme of all things watershed. And, of course, it's even worse news for the coyote.

While wildlife advocates acknowledge that conflicts between coyotes and humans can be unsettling, they are quick to emphasize that, more often than not, the root cause is human behavior, not coyote behavior. Removing a problem animal is sometimes the only solution, but wildlife advocates prefer to educate people rather than eradicate coyotes. They are also quick to provide ample statistics demonstrating that household pets are far more likely to injure humans than are wild animals. As one advocate put it, "You have about as much chance of being bitten by a coyote as you have of being bitten by a shark in your shower."

Right now coyotes appear to be thriving in the Fanno Creek watershed. I've tried for years to photograph them, but on the rare occasion when I've been able to see one, it has vanished before I could even get the lens cap off my camera. I don't know of a documented case of aggressive behavior in any of our local populations, but it won't surprise me if one occurs. Conflict is almost inevitable, as experience with virtually every other species of wild animal inhabiting this watershed clearly shows.

36 Fox TV, Channel 12 (2012)

Bonnie and Clyde

One day I was headed back from a meeting with Brian Wegener of the River-keepers and stopped off at a nearby Starbucks for a late afternoon latte and a little uninterrupted think-time. We'd met to discuss possible approaches toward yet another new threat to Fanno Creek, this one in the form of a two-lane vehicular bridge that would span the stream south of the Tigard City Library. I'd gone into our meeting with a black and white view of how lousy the idea was, but I came out of it feeling both humbled and gray. Brian has a knack for forcing me to think holistically and fairly about issues. In other words, he makes me look at things using the very same watershed approach to problem solving that I try to force others to use. I hate it when he does that.

I was still grinding away on the topic as I left the coffee shop a half hour later. Lost in thought and more or less oblivious to the surroundings, I stepped through the door and was immediately accosted by a pair of mallards. They had been parked just a few feet away from the door in the breezeway that runs between two buildings. They pounced the moment I exited.

"Quack-quack-quack-quack!" which I understood to mean "Your croissant or your life, Suckka!" I tried to reason with them, tried to explain that the flour was just so many empty carbs, that the dairy products would only block their tiny little arteries. It was no use. They backed me up against the wall. Then the hen got nasty. Twice she nibbled at the toe of my shoe. "Quack! Quack!" The drake hung back a couple feet, poised to finish me off if things got out of hand. Finally, in desperation I tore a small chunk off the pastry and flung it towards the patio on my left. They fell for it! While they waddled off to grab the goods I dashed towards my truck.

Who doesn't love a mallard? One of the most successful children's books of all times is about Mrs. Mallard, who ends up having to raise her ducklings in the middle of an urban environment. The book became so popular that the Commonwealth of Massachusetts designated *Make Way for Ducklings* the state's official children's book and placed a statue of the plucky mother duck and her babies on a brick-lined street in the Boston Gardens.[37] These attractive and sometimes comical birds can become very comfortable around humans. They may be one of the first wild animals that a kid in the city has a chance to interact with. They seem so harmless that parents of young children are usually quite at ease around them.

Taking the kids down to the nearest pond or wetland to feed the ducks is one of the more prosaic aspects of urban life, much like feeding pigeons. But noth-

37 The author, Robert McCloskey, said the book was inspired by the ducks that were ubiquitous in the vicinity of the art school he attended in the early 1930s. The Vesper George School of Art was located in Boston's densely populated South End, just a few blocks south of the Charles River.

ing puts a duck in harm's way faster than feeding it on a regular basis.[38] Where such feedings take place the population of waterfowl can swell into the dozens or even the hundreds. If the practice is sustained over a long period of time, other waterfowl may begin to participate. Having waterfowl in wetlands is a good thing, but concentrating them in numbers that can't be maintained by the existing natural resources is not. Situations like this also create serious health concerns for animals and humans. A disease known as avian cholera became established in this area in the 1960s. According to the U.S. Geological Survey National Wildlife Health Center "infections in humans are not uncommon" and "the specific relationship between bird and mammal strains of this bacterium are not well understood.[39]"

Waterfowl and coyotes are just a few of the many kinds of animals living in the Fanno Creek watershed whose behaviors create conflicts with their human neighbors and headaches for wildlife managers. Raccoons and squirrels are very comfortable living in attics if their preferred natural resources are missing from the environment, and will resort to forced entry when the need or opportunity arises. Skunks are well-known for denning under porches and foundations. In the early springtime it is quite common to hear flickers banging away on siding or metal chimney covers as they search for food or nesting sites.

Almost universally despised because of its aggressive feeding habits and its propensity for getting into the engines of jet aircraft, the European starling is yet another creature that will break into an attic if the opportunity occurs. In Oregon the starling is one of the few species of wild animals not protected under the law. But good luck running them off or shooting them. These close relatives of the mynah are among the smartest and fastest learners in the animal kingdom. Because of their adaptability and intelligence, they are almost impossible to eradicate. They consume vast quantities of insects during their reproductive cycle, which would clearly make them a plus if it weren't for the fact that in doing so they are in direct competition with many species of more desirable native birds. Starlings and house sparrows are blamed for the near-extinction of the purple martin.

Nutria are another invasive species that is not protected under Oregon law. Their foraging and burrowing do extensive damage to riparian corridors, putting them at odds with watershed managers and private landowners. Once established in a wetland area this import from South America is extremely hard to control, let alone eradicate. They compete successfully with native populations of beaver and muskrat, and are unwelcome in all parts of the watershed,

38 The slogan, "A fed animal is a dead animal" not only applies to large predators but also to virtually any other kind of wild animal. For those of us who insist on feeding songbirds, the Audubon Society of Portland provides some very useful tips. http://audubonportland.org/wcc/urban/protectingbirds
39 National Wildlife Health Center / USGS (2012).

at least as far as wildlife and watershed managers are concerned. But even the nutria have their fans, as the city of Tigard discovered when crews tried to remove a growing population of the animals from a small set of water retention ponds at the extreme west end of the watershed.

Nutria Nanny

A bioswale is a stormwater treatment facility that relies on natural biological processes to partially clean up stormwater runoff before it enters a river or some other water-body. In essence, these treatment areas are constructed wetlands, designed to provide many of the ecosystem services that a naturally occurring wetland provides. They are a relatively common sight in certain areas of the Fanno Creek watershed, particularly in residential and commercial areas of more recent vintage. One such facility is located on the northwest side of Bull Mountain in Tigard. It's a triangular area, roughly a quarter of an acre in overall area. There's a great deal of scenery packed into the little wetland, including a small pond that overflows into a rocky streambed, which then drains into a large grate at the southwest end of the facility. There's a small island in the center of the pond, and on my last visit a pair of mallards were acting as if they might decide to nest there. The site is well planted, well maintained and the neighbors are lucky to have it around.

A few years ago, a routine inspection of this facility revealed that nutria had gotten into the fenced enclosure that ordinarily keeps such critters away. They had settled in for an extended stay, and judging from the damage to the banks and the surrounding vegetation, more than one family of nutria was living in the place. Crews had gone in to remove the rodents and repair the damage they'd inflicted on the place, but shortly after they set up their traps they discovered that someone was springing them almost as fast as they could be set. Surveillance revealed that an elderly woman in a nearby home was not only springing the traps but had been releasing previously trapped nutria as well. Further investigation revealed that this same neighbor had been feeding the nutria for a considerable length of time. Ultimately, the woman was persuaded that it was necessary for her to stop interfering with the trapping process. The nutria were not just a threat to the integrity of the treatment facility, they crew explained, but also to the downstream sections of the creek as well. They focused her attention on the impact that a failed retention facility might have on the mallards, mergansers and beavers that lived downstream. While they never changed her mind about the nutria, they were able to change her behavior towards them, at least for a while. By the time the trapping came to an end, 34 nutria had been captured.

Nutria don't belong in any of Oregon's watersheds, particularly any as degraded as Fanno Creek; but this clearly had made no difference to their self-appointed benefactor. From her animal-loving perspective, nutria were due the same regard she held for her cats and the other animals she lured into her yard by making food available on an on-demand basis. In her belief system, the freedom and welfare of these destructive rat-kin (and her personal judgment) trumped the environmental concerns, legal rights and municipal authority of the government.

Her perspective and behaviors are not all that unique. A highly publicized incident in 2007 provides an example of the widespread ignorance and disregard that exists in Oregon (and other states, presumably) for legislatively mandated efforts to protect native species. When Oregon Department of Fish and Wildlife (ODFW) moved to seize a pet deer and her fawn from a Molalla family who had failed to obtain the required permits, the agency's actions set off a firestorm of hostile public reaction.[40]

The Snow Ball Syndrome

The deer was named Snow Ball because of her mostly white coat.[41] The family had found her by a roadside in 2001 when she was only a day or two old. Her rear legs were deformed, and they guessed that she had been abandoned by her mother.[42] They scooped her up and took her to a veterinarian. You can argue about how appropriate their actions were up to this point, but I suspect that most people would have behaved similarly. The family's next set of actions are a little less easily understood, however. Somehow they managed to get the veterinarian to put Snowball's crippled legs into casts. Either the veterinarian failed to inform the family of the state's laws regarding the care and keeping of injured wildlife, or they simply decided to ignore them. One way or the other, they took the fawn home and raised it. The deformed little piebald did well enough in her new environment to be mated with another deer the family happened to have around, a blind one called Mr. Magoo.[43] In the fullness of time, Snow Ball gave birth to a fawn of her own, Bucky by name. Happily, Bucky was "normal" in the sense that he looked like most other white-tail deer.

In 2007 an anonymous complaint led county officers and the ODFW to the scene. I've never been able to locate a definitive study of the entire series of events that followed, but as far as I can tell, the family had received notification of the impending seizures and had decided to mount a custody battle even

40 Ross (2007)
41 Piebald deer are not albinos. They suffer from a genetic condition that also predisposes them to a wide variety of bone disorders, including scoliosis.
42 It isn't clear from any of the newspaper reports how they verified that the fawn was indeed abandoned.
43 I could find no information about the origins of Mr. Magoo or how he happened to be in the family's care.

before Snow Ball and Bucky[44] were taken away. When the officers arrived, the media was there and their cameras were already rolling. Within 24 hours the agency and its field officers were being portrayed by local media as a bunch of heartless bastards. In another 24 hours the story had gone viral, the *cause du jour* for talk radio and TV throughout the country.

ODFW and the state's regulations prevailed, but not before the agency endured a terrible beating at the hands of reporters and bloggers in places as far away as Switzerland. The couple filed suit and won the first judgment, only to see it overturned a few months later when the state's appeal was upheld by the Oregon Court of Appeals. By 2008 Bucky (along with his piebald gene-pool) had been released into the wild, and Snow Ball was on her way to a private for-profit animal park in southern Oregon. Some estimates place the cost to taxpayers for the fracas at more than $90,000.

I recall thinking at the time that a great deal of the responsibility for the blowup could be placed on the media, first for its willingness to flame ODFW, and second for an apparent lack of interest in background facts—e.g., what about Mr. Magoo? Where had he come from and why was he blind? How long had the family had him, and what did their allowing him to mate with Snow Ball say about their s environmental sensitivities? I followed the story for a while, but at the time I could not for the life of me see that it had any bearing on my study of Fanno Creek; so I filed my notes in a folder and went on to other inquiries. It was a couple years before I realized that the story was relevant to wildlife management activities taking place right here in the Fanno Creek watershed on a regular basis.

Beaver Battles

At four miles from source to outfall, Summer Creek is the largest of Fanno Creek's major tributaries. It is a perennial stream for the entirety of its length, meaning that from top to bottom measurable quantities of water flow through its channels on a year-round basis. The primary source of this water is a spring that flows out of the ground at the 650-foot level of Cooper Mountain's southern drainage. Just a few hundred feet upstream from its confluence with Fanno Creek, Summer Creek flows through property belonging to the Tigard/Tualatin School District. Fowler Middle School occupies most of the property on the southern side of the creek. Over the last several years, students from this school have reintroduced thousands of Chinook fry into the stream.

Most of the kids understand that there is little chance that any of the hatchlings they release each year will return to spawn in Summer Creek. Even in pre-settlement times Chinook didn't frequent these waters. The stream's tem-

44 According to the couple, Mr. Magoo died shortly after mating with Snow Ball, causes unspecified.

peratures are simply too warm during a critical portion of the species' life cycle for hatchlings to survive long enough even to make it into Tualatin River, just nine miles downstream. Other salmonids continue to be found in the creek from time to time, however, including cutthroat trout and steelhead. The cutthroat trout appear to be particularly adaptable to a wide range of water temperatures and are clearly reproducing in multiple places around the Fanno Creek system. Once in a great while a stray Coho is spotted in the lower reaches, but so far no spawning activity has been observed there for many, many decades.

Multiple factors contribute to Summer Creek's temperature issues. Like all of Fanno Creek's tributaries, the majority of Summer Creek's wetlands, floodplains and adjacent uplands have disappeared under waves of development. Some of the most concentrated residential and commercial areas in Beaverton and Tigard crowd its banks and clutter the hillsides of the mountains that meet to form its main drainage pathway. A few areas bring shaded relief to the stream and its tributaries, most notably a narrow but lush strip of wetlands that runs for almost a half mile through the steep ravines at the western end of Summer Creek's watershed. The dense vegetation here provides a much-needed check to stream temperature during summer months. It also provides quality habitat for a wide variety of creatures, including beaver.

Unfortunately, a great deal of the good this stretch of wetlands might otherwise accomplish is more than offset by the collective impact of five manmade dams that currently clog Summer Creek's arteries. Two of these dams are earthen rigs that intercept the creek's source waters almost immediately after they leave the ground. The remaining three dams are concrete structures spread out along the first three miles of the creek's four-mile run. The largest of these is Summerlake,[45] 12 acres of heat sink that cooks the water and nearly everything in it during the hottest months of the year. As long as these old-fashioned dams remain astride Summer Creek's main stem there is little chance that young salmon will ever swim in its waters for more than a short time immediately after their birth or release.

But not all dams play havoc with the natural cooling processes of the watershed. A short distance downstream from Summerlake is a sixth pond, this one created by a beaver dam that sprawls across the creek just 100 feet upstream from the mouth of a pair of culverts that run under 121st Avenue in Tigard. It's known as Merestone Pond by the neighbors. The pond's surface area varies considerably by season, but on average it is around two acres. The total area of the pond and its associated wetlands is around 15 acres. The beaver dam and most of its wetlands are situated on property belonging to the city of Tigard. A

45 While it is called a lake, Summerlake is more accurately described as a pond because it is not deep enough to contain water that escapes heating from direct sunlight. Except for the one created by the beaver, which is predominantly a wetland, all the other impoundments on Summer Creek are ponds.

major portion of the property abutting the southern boundary of the wetlands belongs to the city of Tigard as well, including the grounds of Mary Woodward Elementary School and a triangular section at the west end of the pond called The Summerlake Natural Area. Bordering the pond to the north are a dozen neighbors, all of whom enjoy unobstructed views of the wetlands from the rear windows and back decks of their homes.

One of the principal benefits of having a beaver pond in your backyard is that the wetlands habitat it creates usually develops into a highly diversified plant and animal community. The longer the pond continues to be serviced by the beaver, the richer and more stable these communities become. The wetlands can become spectacular wildlife viewing areas if they are allowed to mature long enough. And whereas traditionally designed, human-built dams tend to reduce salmonid populations, beaver dams tend to enhance them. There are aesthetic benefits associated with living close to beaver action as well, particularly if your home is well above the level of any conceivable dam height. The homeowners along this particular reach of the creek have reaped those ecological and aesthetic benefits. But the city of Tigard, the owner and custodian of the wetlands as well as the roadway and culvert occasionally threatened by beaver activity, has been far less fortunate. For years now, about all the city's been able to reap where the beaver dam is concerned has been frequent criticism from the Merestone neighbors for its land and animal management practices.

The beaver is a much-loved and admired animal—the stuff of legend, lore and myth. Its reputation for hard work and good citizenship is unequalled in the animal kingdom. However, in some situations the beaver's behaviors can create conditions that threaten the property and even the safety of its human neighbors. For this reason its status as a game animal in Oregon is somewhat paradoxical. For example, the Oregon Department of Agriculture classifies beavers as predators because they are rodents and sometimes destroy crops—orchard trees for example. As a result, it is permissible to remove them from private property using lethal means without first obtaining a permit.[46] On the other hand, Oregon Department of Fish and Wildlife classifies the beaver as a fur-bearing animal, which means that a permit must be acquired prior to trapping or otherwise removing them from public lands. The most important take-away here, so far as understanding the beaver's status on either public or private property, is that it is a *regulated, but not a protected,* species.

Because beaver are so generally admired and their legal status so poorly understood by the average city dweller, their management in the urban context is particularly difficult. It is a foregone conclusion that agencies and individuals who must resolve issues involving beavers and their dams will receive at least

46 They may be live-trapped and moved to another location so long as a formal permitting protocol is observed and the appropriate permit is obtained.

as much criticism for their efforts as praise, sometimes decidedly more. That goes doubly when the actions taken are proactive rather than reactionary. This became the situation for Tigard a few months ago, when crews arrived at 121st Avenue and began dismantling what they had determined was an abandoned dam. According to press accounts[47] of the incident and its aftermath, the city decided to remove the dam in order to ensure that debris[48] from the site would not pose a blockage problem for downstream flows, particularly through the culvert that runs underneath 121st Avenue.

It's easy to see why the city might be anxious about the dam. The danger of flooding in this low-lying corridor between Bull Mountain to the south and Cooper Mountain to the north is very real, even when the culvert is clear of debris. Summer Creek is the principal drainage for an area of approximately four and a half square miles, or around 15 percent of the total Fanno Creek watershed. During one of the heavy rain events typical in this area of the Tualatin Basin, it is not at all unusual for this part of the watershed to experience an inch or two of rainfall in a 24-hour period. This means that once or twice in a given year the creek must handle about 75 million gallons of water[49] in close to a 24-hour period. That's significant enough, but a great deal of the water begins its journey at elevations from 100 to 500 feet higher than the streambed that must carry it. This means that in addition to being large in volume, the water is also moving very fast.

Beaver dams are quite often blown apart during such rain events, and it this feature that provokes so much concern on the part of Tigard's watershed managers. A serious breaching of the dam on 121st Street could send all kinds of woody debris and mud directly into the mouth of the twin culverts that lie less than a hundred feet away. Once blocked, the roadway would become a dam in its own right, one that would be significantly higher and more substantial than the beaver dam. Culverts are designed to pass water through their structures, not over or around them. Once a culvert is overwhelmed it is quite possible that its footings, and ultimately the roadway itself, will be destroyed.[50] This kind of catastrophe can create major damage to property, disrupt communications, and take human lives. When such catastrophes might have been avoidable to

47 Pursinger (2011)
48 A spokesman for the city noted that the dam had breached well before the city took action. When crews went out to inspect it at that time the pond had mostly vanished. "Once the water level dropped, it appeared people—not beavers—had attempted to rebuild a portion of the dam with a tarp, pallets and other materials."
49 The actual total would be 150 million, but even in its current state of development the watershed is still able to absorb around half of the amount. In pre-settlement times only the most significant rain storms, the legendary 100-year events, would have produced more runoff than the creek might be able to take in stride.
50 A video of such a collapse at a very similar site in Freeport, Maine went viral on YouTube in 2008 and is still downloadable at http://www.youtube.com/watch?v=p_uqPR4Ir5o.

begin with, the legal and liability consequences can be staggering, as well.[51]

Because it owns the road and the drainage corridor, the city is obligated to do all it can to ensure that the culvert is never breached. It makes sense, then, that when the dam suddenly appeared to be abandoned the city decided to seize the moment and clear it away. It can also be argued that by removing what it believed was an abandoned dam, one known to cause culvert blockages in the past, the city was merely meeting its safety responsibilities proactively. Given today's hyper-litigious society, the case can even be made that, should such flooding ever occur, the city might still run the risk of being sued by nearby residents for failing to take the necessary steps to prevent it.

To what degree neighbors living on the north bank of the pond were aware of the city's concerns isn't clear; but when several of them showed up at a City Council meeting later that month, they arrived with the clear intention of taking the city to task. The citizens expressed anger over what the removal of the dam and the subsequent draining of the pond might mean to the aesthetic component of their property values. They were also upset by what they perceived as a breakdown in basic communication between the city of Tigard and the community. In a newspaper report of the meeting, the city's assistant public works director commented, "We could have done a better job of notifying the entire neighborhood that we were going to do this work."[52]

Nearby residents were not the only group who took issue with the city's removal of the dam and its perceived lack of communication skills. ODFW did not learn about the dam's removal until after it had taken place. The agency immediately expressed concern over the timing of the removal and its potential impact on other species that share the habitat with the beaver, including eagles that nest in nearby areas. The city had elected to forego notifying ODFW because it did not consider the removal of an abandoned dam to be a serious issue. But ODFW's concerns were related to the timing of the action, rather than to the action itself.

There are seasonal constraints on the conduct of in-stream projects on streams such as Summer Creek. These constraints were established to protect downstream habitat from "sediment releases and downstream channel scouring..."[53] While the state agency was critical of the city's actions, and while such criticism usually carries some persuasive force, in this instance the agency has little actual regulatory authority over the area because, regardless of the

51 The inspection well for a major sewage connection lies immediately downstream from the dam. A huge amount of raw sewage flows through this junction on a constant basis. What might happen to this structure and the pipes below if the dam should ever fail in a major flood is something to be genuinely worried about. It could be an ecological calamity as well an engineering nightmare.
52 Florip (2011)
53 Oregon Administrative Rule 629-660-050.

Merestone Pond—the beaver dam at SW 121st prior to demolition by the city of Tigard

Beaver deceiver—modifications at the site designed to entice dam building further upstream

occasional presence of cutthroat trout and steelhead, Summer Creek is not currently classified by the state as being "essential salmonid habitat."[54]

Shortly after the dam was removed, neighbors reported seeing beaver activity in the area; shortly after that, further reports indicated that those same beaver were back at work on the dam. Those claims bear further investigation because it is not uncommon for neighbors to help out Mother Nature by rebuilding sections of beaver dams themselves. But whether or not the beaver have actually returned, there's little doubt that return they will. This particular dam has been torn down and rebuilt multiple times in the past. Accordingly, Tigard is hard at work on a plan for modifications to the site that may encourage the beaver to rebuild further upstream from the culverts. The success of these modifications remains to be seen.

The incidents I've described above highlight some of the more significant challenges watershed professional face when dealing with wildlife issues in urban environments.[55] Chief among these are (1) differing cultural values about the sanctity of animal life; (2) gross misconceptions about what constitutes appropriate behaviors towards wild animals; (3) blatant disregard and/or latent hostility toward wildlife regulations and those who enforce them; (4) conflicting community perspectives related to the goals of wildlife management; (5) jurisdictional disconnects (communications); (6) conflicting jurisdictional priorities; and (7) fragmentation of responsibilities and/or authority. My schooling in all of these began when my study took me into some of the most important wetlands areas remaining in the watershed.

54 Oregon Department of State Lands (2012)
55 Hadidian et al (1997)

Discarded grocery cart in Tigard's Fanno Creek Park

UP FANNO CREEK

5—Political Science

Tigardville

On a roadmap the intersection of Highways 217 and 99W creates an "X" marking an area where transportation corridors leading in and out of the Tualatin Valley have intersected for thousands of years. In prehistoric times timbered uplands here gave way to the upper margins of ancient Fanno Creek's flourishing wetlands. Given the lay of the land and its pivotal location, it was inevitable that sometime after the Pioneers arrived, a city would be established in this area. "East Butte," early settlers called this transportation hub, presumably because it lay at the base of a 500-foot bluff, part of the larger Bull Mountain that dominates this portion of the watershed. When Wilson Tigard and his family arrived here in 1852 most of the Donation Land Claims had been gobbled up, so he had to purchase the deed to his 320 acres from an earlier settler.

Almost from the outset the Tigards figured significantly in the development of the area. Wilson was a Republican and, like his nearby neighbor, Augustus Fanno, was deeply opposed to slavery and said so in a letter back to his relatives in Arkansas:

> *...there is no country more favorable for slaves to make their escape from their masters than Oregon and there are plenty of us that is not too good to assist them in getting away if they [the Democrats] should make it [Oregon] a slave state.*[56]

The Tigard family also became involved in organizing and building the East Butte School.[57] Then in 1880, Wilson's son Charles built a general store that also served as a meeting hall for the small farming community. A post office came to the store in 1886 and the area was officially designated as Tigardville. The Tigard's general store was the cultural and physical center of the community until 1910, when the Oregon Electric Railway came to the area. The best location for track turned out to be along Fanno Creek's eastern corridor, and the center of Tigardville's commercial and civic activities soon shifted in that direction, leaving the general store on the periphery of the town. Then, as now, Fanno Creek ran straight through the heart of the community.

To the entrepreneurs who ran the railroad, the name "Tigardville" was too easily confused with nearby Wilsonville, so they shortened it to Tigard. The community grew slowly at first after the arrival of the railroad. Roughly equidistant from Portland and Oregon City, Tigard was situated between the two main markets for Washington County's agricultural bounty. But the Tualatin River was an unreliable shipping route and most of the nearest roads sturdy

56 Bourke & DeBats (1995)
57 Oregon Encyclopedia (2012)

BOOK TWO   167

enough to handle commerce led to Oregon City. As a result, Tigard kept its rural character until well after its main street was paved in 1930. By 1961, when the residents finally voted to incorporate, the population was still less than 2,000.[58]

For Tigard and other small communities in the eastern portion of the Tualatin River Basin, the 1960s ushered in an era of rapid economic development and urban growth that continues to this day. By the end of the millennium more than 38,000 people called Tigard home. Most of the farmland and open spaces that had been hallmarks of the community for more than 150 years were gone, buried under a rolling wave of roadways, malls, housing developments, business parks and commercial facilities.

Tigard treated its portion of the Fanno Creek wetlands and floodplains the way other communities treated their areas of the watershed during the same period—as the area developed, the creek's wetlands and floodplains suffered a considerable amount of environmental abuse. The level of degradation was compounded by the fact that the portion of Fanno Creek that flows through Tigard drops less than fifty feet between Main Street and the Fanno/Tualatin River confluence, five miles further downstream. Because water flows very slowly through this stretch, sediment and pollutants settle out at relatively higher rates. As a result, Tigard's portion of the watershed has borne the brunt of accelerating development taking place further upstream in Beaverton and Portland.

Luckily for Tigard, and for Fanno Creek as well, the city's more recent growth has taken place since passage of the Clean Water Act (1972) and Oregon State Bill 100 (1973). A landmark bill in every sense of the word, osb 100 created a structure for statewide planning that required every municipality to create, and then implement, a comprehensive plan for its future growth that would be consistent with statewide goals and planning guidelines. Passage of the bill was driven both by economic and environmental concerns. The state was not benefiting enough economically from its natural resources, even as those resources were being driven to the brink of destruction. Planning and vision—or more precisely, the lack thereof at every level of government—was identified as the root cause of the problem. osb 100, it was hoped, would provide that vision, as well as a comprehensive structure that would lead toward a more effective approach to land use decisions.

The bill originally identified 14 statewide planning goals[59] that ran the gamut from Citizen Involvement (Goal 1) to Urbanization (Goal 14). Municipalities were then compelled to draw up comprehensive plans and accompanying sup-

58 Population 43,035 in 2010.
59 Five more were ultimately added to deal with specific concerns including the Willamette River Greenway and coastal resources.

port materials[60] based on consideration of the statewide goals. The Department of Land Conservation and Development[61] (DLCD) would then review these plans and, if necessary, send them back to the respective municipalities for further revision, an exercise that continued until the DLCD considered the plans to be in compliance with the statewide goals and guidelines. Throughout the entire process multiple opportunities were presented for citizen review and input. It was a lengthy, difficult and expensive process for many of the cities, and it wasn't until 1986 (more than a dozen years after the law was enacted) that every city and county in the state stood in compliance with the basic directives.

Tigard completed its first iteration of the comprehensive plan process in 1983, and substantially overhauled it in 2007. The DLCD reviewed the new plan and determined that it was compliant with statewide planning goals. This latest version is 252 pages long, but reads easily, and generally describes how Tigard plans to move forward within the framework of applicable state goals.[62] It is designed to meet foreseeable challenges of the next 20 years but makes it clear that tomorrow's unknowns can change today's certainties. The document also clarifies the role of the comprehensive plan in the city's actual decision-making process where land use issues may be concerned:

> ...state law does not allow comprehensive plan policies to be directly used as decision making criteria for most land use decisions. In order for comprehensive plan policies to be applicable to decisions...they must first be translated into clear and objective standards such as those found in the *Tigard Community Development Code.*[63]

Above all else, the document is intended to represent "the land use vision and values of the community." In some cases those values and visions are expressed as "mandatory statements," while others have "more aspirational qualities." What this means in practice is that, so far as the Tigard Community Development Code is concerned, any of the various goals and objectives articulated by the document may be used as decision-making criteria, if and when the City Council or the planning commission so choose. "Ultimately, it is at the discretion of the City's elected leadership whether or not some policy statements versus others are applicable to given circumstances." I ran into one of those "given circumstances" when I showed up in front of the city's planning commission and offered testimony against a proposed change to the Code.

60 Community development or building code, regulatory maps special area plans and the like.
61 The DLCD is guided by the LCDC. In essence the LCDC is the conscience and the DLCD is the arm of the state's land use planning activities.
62 Tigard is responsible for meeting 12 of the 19 Statewide Land Use Planning Goals.
63 Page I-2 of the Introduction to Tigard's 2007 Comprehensive Plan.

18.775 etc.

Around the same time that Tigard began work on the development of its current Comprehensive Plan, it also began work on an ambitious Downtown Improvement Plan.[64] In essence, the Plan is designed to revitalize the city's "under-utilized core" by attracting high-quality commercial and residential development to what is currently a concentration of light industry and small mixed use or residential complexes. One of its more critical components is called "The Fanno Creek Park and Plaza Master Plan." Conceptually this master plan established the "Green Heart" identified in the Downtown Improvement Plan "by locating the primary open space and plaza between downtown and the community's unique natural resource—Fanno Creek."

A portion of the park, along with an aged and inadequate trail system, already existed between Main Street and Hall Boulevard. The plan not only called for the renovation of this existing parkland but also included the development of several acres of open land near the Tigard Library that was partially comprised of floodplain. Wetlands advocates were of two minds about the plan. On one hand, it called for extensive restoration work in areas that would really benefit from the upgrade. The trail system was in particularly poor condition and had been developed well before the passage of legislation designed to protect wetlands and floodplains. But wetlands advocates were concerned that sections of the proposed new trails would run through some of the lowest and most sensitive areas of the floodplain. They were also troubled by another undesirable trail design element: some sections created loops through wildlife habitat, compromising sunning and breeding areas for one of the last known populations of native turtles remaining in the watershed. The plan was being redesigned to address as many of these concerns as possible when the planners discovered an even greater flaw in the overall trail design. Because major segments of the new and *already approved* trail plan would be built through low-lying areas prone to annual flooding, they could not be permitted under the city's own building code.

For a while this discovery seriously complicated things for the city and its planning staff. The Fanno Creek Park and Plaza Master Plan was "necessary for implementation of projects as defined in the City Center Urban Renewal Plan, adopted by City Council and approved by voters in May 2006." If the plan could not be implemented, then what would be the political and budgetary fallout from what was apparently a planning oversight?

The matter simply hung there for a time. Then, after studying the most critical portion of the code involved, the city's planners determined that the key language was essentially meaningless. Therefore, they maintained, it could

64 Tigard Urban Renewal Plan.

simply be stricken from the Community Development Code without causing serious harm to either the spirit or the rule of the code's sensitive lands provisions. With that meaningless language out of the way there would be nothing to stop the projects from going forward.

In another era the offending section of the code might have vanished in the blink of an eye and without much, if any, public notice. However, provisions in OSB 100 require that amendments to municipal codes go through a public review process before being enacted. As a first step in this process planners send their recommendations to the city's Planning Commission for review and subsequent recommendation to the City Council. This structure creates a minimum of two formal opportunities for public comment and debate on any given code amendment.

On a chilly February evening in 2009, members of the Tigard Planning Commission[65] began wrestling in public with "Development Code Amendment 2008-00005." If you've ever served on such a commission you'll immediately recognize that their task that night was not a particularly enviable one. First the commissioners would have to get their heads around a fairly substantial and complex package of planning documents and related information. Then they would listen to arguments presented by the planning staff that favored the removal, as well as any counter arguments from the public. Finally, once testimony had been collected, the commission would have to deliberate and then decide on one of three courses of action:

- send the proposal forward to the City Council with a recommendation for approval;
- send the proposal forward to the City Council with a recommendation for disapproval;
- send the proposal back to the planning department for additional work.

I arrived for the meeting an hour early. It had been more than a year since I last walked the portions of the creek that would be at the center of the evening's discussions, and I wanted to refresh my physical memory of the wetlands involved. I went into the old section of the park at the Main Street entrance and headed east towards Hall Boulevard. Over six miles of the Fanno Creek's main stem and another twenty miles or more of its tributaries flow through Tigard's city limits, but this is the best reach for getting a good sense of the close physical and economic relationship between the city and the creek. Tigard's central business district is built around more than 25 acres of heavily degraded floodplain straddling the stream.

---

65 Commission members are appointed by the City Council for terms of four years each. They perform in an advisory capacity and serve without compensation.

POLITICAL SCIENCE

Depending upon the season Fanno Creek either trickles, glides, or thunders into town from the northwest. At Main Street it passes under a small bridge, then speeds east towards Hall Boulevard, a half mile away. After its passage under Hall Street the creek makes a wide turn to the south, meanders past the east end of the new Tigard Library, then heads for its confluence with the Tualatin River, three miles of stream channel further to the south.

It's a short walk from Main Street to Hall Boulevard, and I was at the street crossing before I realized it. Usually I am all eyes and ears on these walks, but on this occasion I barely noted the wooden bridges I crossed, or the long-abandoned remains of an encampment set up by homeless folk, or the standing puddles of water left over from the heavy rains just a few days ago. My mind was grinding away in anticipation of the meeting and how best to make my case to the commissioners. One approach was to simply turn my memo over to the commission's secretary, who would distribute copies to the commissioners. That would save me the discomfort of speaking publicly, but it would also significantly reduce the opportunity to learn something about the commissioners by watching their reactions to my verbal testimony. One way or the other, I had a lot to talk about, and nowhere near enough time to make my case.[66]

The details of the proposed code amendment had become available on the city's website several days earlier. I downloaded a copy and went right to work on a memo to the planning commission. I hoped it might help convince the group to reject the proposal outright, or at least send it back to the planning department for more work. I already knew that protecting wetlands from development using arguments based upon environmental or ecological considerations was an uphill battle.[67] Instead, I elected to take on the planning staff's rationale one point at a time, using counter-arguments based mostly on common sense.

Somehow I had managed to keep these arguments within the confines of a two-page memo. But the question remained: Should I just hand it to the secretary before the meeting? Or should I attempt to amplify its key points by testifying? What kind of experience would it be to deliver my remarks orally? I have spoken to quite a few groups in the past, some of them fairly large and a couple of them somewhat hostile. I usually handled the chore okay, but it was always a very stressful experience and I was rarely pleased with my efforts. Still, in this case I thought actually testifying publicly might provide my arguments with a little more persuasive force. In the end I decided to speak out against the proposed amendment with my own voice. That's the way Augustus

66 In most cases those testifying are allocated from three to five minutes in which to deliver their arguments. Individuals used to giving testimony in front of government bodies use memos to provide more in-depth arguments and then use their allotment of minutes to press key points.
67 Such areas are also critical aspects of a municipality's social and psychological infrastructure, of course, but advocating for sane developmental practices on such "subjective" criteria has proved ineffective for quite some time now.

172   UP FANNO CREEK

Fanno, Wilson Tigard, and the other citizens in these parts would have done it during their era, I reminded myself.

I arrived in the main assembly room just in time to sign up as an "against" before the commissioners began to file in and take their seats. The turnout was very small, which surprised and disappointed me. I considered this amendment a big deal, but aside from the commissioners and the city's staff, only half a dozen people were in attendance. Two in the front row turned out to be city planners. A third person, a reporter from the local paper, sat in the very back, just a few chairs away from the exit. Three more people were seated in the middle section of the room, Watershed Folk that I knew quite well. We exchanged quick hellos as the commissioners stood and led everyone in the Pledge of Allegiance. After some organizational housekeeping, the commission got right down to business by asking "Staff" to provide the specifics of the amendment. The staff person rolled out the issues in a very straightforward manner.[68]

Title 18 of the Tigard Community Development Code deals with all land use development considerations. It is comprised of eight separate chapters that detail operations, policies, procedures, zoning considerations and specific standards for land development under all kinds of conditions. Chapter .775 addresses "Sensitive Lands" and contains 13 sections, each dealing with a particular set of land use provisions as these relate to areas such as the floodplains along Fanno Creek. Broadly stated, the overall purpose of Chapter 18.775 is to preserve and maintain the integrity and functionality of lands generally unsuitable for development because they (1) lie within the 100 year floodplain; (2) constitute natural drainageways; (3) are wetlands areas regulated by other agencies; (4) comprise significant fish and wildlife habitat. It does this by spelling out, in considerable detail, the criteria related to three categories of use: permitted, prohibited and nonconforming.

Section .070 talks about Sensitive Land Permits, which are required before any development may legally occur within sensitive lands. The section contains language that nicely illustrates why many people refuse even to consider tackling these kinds of documents: "Depending on the nature and intensity of the proposed activity...either a Type II or Type III permit is required as delineated in Sections 18.775.020.F and 18.775.020.G. The approval criteria...are presented in Sections 18.775.070.B—18.775.070.E below." This isn't actually too bad on its face, but when you get to 18.775.020.F you quickly discover that Type II procedures are governed by Section 18.390.040. This is potentially madden-

---

68 The sketch that follows was distilled from my notes. The verbatim testimony is part of the public record and may be obtained from the city of Tigard.

ing information because in all likelihood you didn't happen to pick up that part of the document on your way out of City Hall.[69]

Five paragraphs are developed under Section .070, including Paragraph .B, which explains the Code as it relates to development within the 100-year floodplain. At the bottom of this top-down assemblage sits Article .5, one of seven other articles under Paragraph .B that address highly specific aspects of developing within the floodplain. This is how the entire section of code looks in diagrammatic form:

Title—18

Chapter—.775

Section—.070

Paragraph—.B

Article—.5[70]

Article .5, the subject of the proposed amendment, specifically prohibits the development of pedestrian and bicycle pathways in areas that are "below the elevation of an average annual flood." Apart from the creek bed itself, these are the lowest and most ecologically sensitive sections in the entire 100-year floodplain.[71] They are regularly inundated one or more times a year, sometimes to considerable depth.

Into the Breach

I had somehow expected staff to skirt what I considered the most damning aspect of the entire proposition: Article .5 had to go simply because it was getting in the way of plans to construct trails through sensitive lands. Much to my surprise the Director of Redevelopment had elected to go right at it in a memo to the planners dated January 12, 2009:

> One aspect of the master plan calls for the realignment of trails to allow the public to access and appreciate natural areas of the park that are currently inaccessible. Without approval of this amendment it would not be possible to construct Fanno Creek Park as approved in the adopted master plan.

The planners had dutifully picked up this language and repeated it almost word for word in their brief to the Planning Commission. To their credit, they also came up with a few other, less Machiavellian reasons for getting rid of .5:

- The original intent of B.5 is unclear;
- Locating trails and bicycle paths in areas inundated on a regular basis does not pose a threat to sensitive habitat areas;

69 The city's website lists ten web pages for 18.390.040, all of which refer to the statute but none of which explain how it works. ARRRRGGGGHHHH!

70 In terms of overall importance, Articles are somewhat analogous to the fine print in a mortgage contract.

71 Areas designated as "100 Year Floodplains" have a 1% chance (1 chance in 100) of being filled with water in any given year.

- Removal of this section supports statewide planning Goal 5.

A few of the commissioners questioned the city staff about some minor details, and then the public comment period commenced. These municipal processes are conducted along quasi-judicial lines. The commissioners would be acting as judges, rather than policy or law-makers. The process would be open to public input, up to the point where the commission's president determined that sufficient testimony had been heard, at which point the proceedings would be formally closed to public input and deliberations would begin. An interesting feature of this process is that while closed to further public input, the deliberations take place in the public eye.

Other than the city staff personnel who testified at the beginning of the meeting, no one else came forward to support the proposed amendment. As a result, I was the first citizen to go on record that night. As I made my way up to the microphone on the table in front of the commission, I cursed myself for getting into this predicament. Once seated, I gave my name, address and occupation, then launched into the key points of my presentation.[72]

I wish I could say that my testimony was riveting and helped save the day for Article B.5, as well as the many streams in Tigard that its framers must have had in mind when they crafted it a few decades back. Truth be known, it was a far more nerve-wracking experience than I had anticipated. I don't recall much of what I said, or if any of it was presented in a coherent manner or had much impact. I had my talking-points and my memo in front of me, and if I followed either of them to any extent, I almost surely made the following case for keeping Article .5 intact:

- Wetlands that flood regularly are called floodplains, and as such are designated as being sensitive lands by both federal and state agencies. Next to the actual streambeds themselves, these often-inundated areas are home to countless species of plants and animals;
- Locating trails and bicycle paths in such areas clearly poses a threat to the safety of wildlife located in them, and in doing so also degrades the overall functionality of the wetlands itself;
- Removing the protections that .5 provides to these sensitive wetlands is contrary to the spirit and the letter of Statewide Planning Goal 5, the express purpose of which is "to protect natural resources and conserve scenic and historic areas and open spaces."
- Removing this section (.5) from the code simply because it "is necessary in order to support an already-approved development plan" strongly

---

72 The reconstruction that follows is a brief outline of what I discussed with commission members that night. They were gracious enough to give me more than 10 minutes of presentation time that evening. As these kinds of activities go that was far more than generous.

suggests that vital organs of the city's government are less interested in political integrity than they are in political expediency.

The commissioners thanked me politely for my public involvement and then invited me to return to my seat. As I lurched back to my chair, my fellow wetlands advocates gave me encouraging looks, and one of them patted me on the arm. Then each in turn got up and gave their own testimony. They were all veterans of this process, and also well-known by the commissioners and staff. Each came at the amendment from different directions, but at bottom they all agreed on a couple fundamental points. First, completely removing the article's protections from some of the most sensitive lands in the watershed could have a potentially devastating impact on the ecological health of the stream corridor. Secondly, if the proposed amendment couldn't be dumped totally, the commission should refer the matter back to the planning department, with instructions to reword the article in such a way that it could achieve its basic purpose without jeopardizing any essential elements of the downtown plan.

When all the testimony had been collected,[73] the commission's president closed the hearing to public participation, and the commissioners began to deliberate. At first it felt odd to be suddenly left out of the process and placed in a situation where, for all intents and purposes, we simply had ceased to exist. But as the discussion intensified, I began to feel as if I were watching a play. Seven of the nine commissioners were present, but only a few actually spoke their minds. Very quickly it became clear, from both direction of the conversation and the body-language of those who chose to keep silent that no one was going to back the idea of dumping the proposed amendment. At the same time, it was also clear that several of the commissioners were unwilling to send the existing package to the City Council for approval. For a while there was an effort to alter the amendment right there on the spot.

Most of the commissioners seemed well versed in the issues and the process details, but a couple were clearly struggling with some of the finer points. As the group continued working towards anything they could put to a motion, I began wondering about key details of the deliberative process, particularly the methods used to select and school candidates for the commission. These individuals had all been appointed by the Tigard City Council; what kind of selection criteria had the councilors used to ensure that the people they selected would be effective planning commissioners?[74]

As the discussion continued and the evening wore on, I was reminded how difficult, and sometimes thankless, it can be to serve on public committees or

73 The Portland Audubon Society also gave testimony against the proposed amendment. Their remarks were delivered in a memo mailed to the commission several days prior to the meeting.
74 There is information about the roles and responsibilities of commissioners on the city's website, but nothing that speaks to the selection criteria or process.

commissions. I'd only been on a couple myself, and none of them carried anything like the burden of responsibility that a planning commission must bear. If you ask people why they volunteer for this kind of *pro bono* service to the community you'll get several answers. For most it's about "giving something back to the community." They are grateful for the privilege and the opportunity to help manage the community's resources and issues. Some view this kind of service as a good way to learn more about the processes of local government, and use it to further their political aspirations. For the latter group, serving on a planning commission like this is more than simply a matter of resume building. Wrestling with tough issues such as the one the commissioners were addressing tonight is a great way to develop the arts of communication and compromise.

At around 10:30 the commission reached consensus on a motion that sent the whole package back to planning. The planners were instructed to come up with new language for Article 5 that wouldn't scuttle the Downtown Plan, but might also preserve some of the protections provided by the current language. As we filed out of the meeting, I asked one of my friends how he felt about the decision.

"It's a good start, he said, "but the devil is in the details. We'll just have to see what they come up with and take it from there. The good news tonight is that they didn't simply run over the code, which they might have if we hadn't been here to offer our two cents."

A few weeks later, the planners presented the Planning Commission with two options they maintained would balance competing benefits (recreational use vs. natural resources) on a site-specific basis. Both options did little to actually protect the wetlands, but one of them would at least require the city to conduct a wildlife assessment "to ensure that the proposed [trail] alignment minimizes impacts to significant wildlife habitat." To the disappointment of those still opposed to the gutting of the provision's initial language, this particular revision satisfied the Planning Commission's desire for a compromise. They voted unanimously to recommend approval of the amended language.

A few days later, I conducted an informal poll of the Watershed Folk who had attended both meetings and asked how they felt about the outcome. All were disappointed, but more than half of them believed that, because of the mitigation work that would still be required in order to site the trails in the wetlands, the compromise would actually bring "net environmental benefits" to the wetlands involved. I reflected on their "glass half full" argument for a bit and then decided to reject it. I couldn't see how the wetlands could benefit in any meaningful sense of "net-gain" when in point-of-fact the new and/or redesigned pathways would take up square-footage that had once been—or had the potential to be—untrampled mud and native vegetation.

Battleground—the wetlands at Wall Street

By then I had become convinced that loss of actual footprint was the single greatest challenge facing Fanno Creek. The overall distance from the creek's headwaters and its confluence with the Tualatin River hasn't changed much in the last two hundred years, but the dimensions of its wetlands and floodplains have changed radically in that span. Those changes have been more extensive in some areas than in others, and large portions of the most critical parts of the watershed have simply winked out of existence. "Fragmentation" is what it's called in the language of the Urban Stream Syndrome.[75] The effects of fragmentation on habitat can be dramatic; but less obvious are its equally catastrophic effects on the water-processing capacities of the floodplains and wetlands that comprise the heart and soul of a creek.

For a while after that evening in 2009 I became a frequent visitor to Tigard's planning meetings, and on a couple of occasions I even attended a few City Council meetings focused on wetlands issues. In the process I was gaining an even deeper awareness of the intense pressure placed on the watershed by development. I was also learning that the regulatory structure that is supposed to protect and preserve these areas from most of that pressure is not generally up to the task.

A Bridge to Nowhere

On August 16, 2010, Tigard's Planning Commission heard arguments for and against "Comprehensive Plan Amendment (CPA) 2009-0004/Sensitive Lands Review (SLR) 2009-0004/Adjustment (VAR) 2010-0002-Wall Street Extension (FIELDS)." The commission was charged with the task of listening to arguments for and against the application and the amendment to code it entailed. At the end of the process the commission would make a formal recommendation to the City Council to either reject the application or move forward with the necessary code amendment.

The applicant, Mr. Fred Fields, had filed for permits related to the construction of a 320-foot long, two-lane bridge from the end of the Wall Street stub to his property on the other side of Fanno Creek. Fields owned a 25-acre site that had somehow been cut-off from direct access to any of the existing roadways in the area. He needed the bridge to make developing the property feasible. A portion of the proposed bridge would occupy the wetlands just east of the end of the stub. Tigard had included protections for such wetlands in the "sensitive lands" provisions of its building code, and these provisions could not be removed without first amending the document that drives the code—the Comprehensive Plan.

75 Walsh et al (2005)

If the City Council chose to approve the amendment, it in turn would be required to gain approval for the change from the state's Land Conservation and Development Commission. Such approvals are usually granted, but only after the municipality mounts a convincing argument before the commission. The process is further complicated by the fact that any opponents to the proposed amendment may present counter arguments through the public hearings that are required for every major step in the process.

The meeting on August 16 represented the first step in the amendment process, and it must have been clear to the commissioners from the moment they filed into the room that a real battle was brewing. Town Hall, the site of such hearings, was packed with a standing-room-only crowd consisting primarily of opponents to the bridge. More than 75 people from neighborhoods close to the proposed site were on hand, along with another dozen wetlands advocates from a half dozen local environmental organizations. Letters and emails arguing against the proposed amendment had been arriving in Tigard's planning office for several days prior to the meeting, so the city's officials had anticipated a large turnout. But even the extra chairs they had provided would not accommodate everyone, so more had to be brought out of storage.

The hearing began with arguments "for" the proposed amendment. The Fields team's presentation moved forward along two distinct pathways, one economic and the other environmental. First, they suggested that the city would profit significantly, both from the construction of the bridge and from the subsequent development of the 25-acre property that the bridge would make accessible from the Hall Boulevard transportation corridor. Bridge-building was a costly enterprise, they noted, and would create employment opportunities for the community. Finally, the development of the property would provide the city with new residents and new revenues from additional property taxes. The applicant would pay for the building of the bridge; the city would be responsible only for long-term maintenance of the bridge and the adjoining roadway.

Along with this economic carrot the Fields team held out an environmental rutabaga. The team began by acknowledging that the stream corridor might be subject to short-term impacts due to the bridge construction; but, they maintained, anticipated adherence to BMPs[76] made such damage unlikely. If any damage did occur, it would be "temporary." Furthermore, despite any such temporary damages the city could anticipate that "long-term impacts to the stream and adjacent habitat areas *could very well* (italics mine) have positive aspects." The area was already so highly degraded, the team maintained, that construction of the bridge would actually result in a healthier ecosystem:

---

76 Best Management Practices. Many Watershed Folk I've talked to believe that where public or private development projects are concerned, this acronym should be changed to LMPs: Least Management Practices.

...the City and Clean Water Services would require significant mitigation of wetland impacts, suggesting that the ultimate condition of the Fanno Creek corridor would improve as a result of the roadway extension.[77]

Testimony against the proposed amendment came from 16 interested parties, including nearby property owners, apartment dwellers and local environmentalists. Some—particularly among the local residents—were obviously uncomfortable with public speaking. Most had prepared for their presentations, but that didn't keep their voices from quivering a little as they spoke their minds. The more experienced speakers tended to be professionals with conservation or watershed management backgrounds. A couple of them were local residents, and they struck me as the most effective speakers of the lot; they easily blended the various counter-arguments together into a single, powerful thread.

Those counter-arguments were fairly simple. First, nearby residents were concerned about the impact the bridge would have on their property values and view-rights. They had been attracted to the neighborhood largely because of the physical and aesthetic amenities the nearby creek corridor provided. Damaging that environment would also damage the resale value of their homes. Another factor likely to affect property values, and human safety, as well, they maintained, was the anticipated increase in vehicular congestion at the library, already one of the busiest areas in Tigard.

Finally, many of those arguing against the amendment, myself included, contended that the Fields team's arguments related to both the economic benefits (high gain) and environmental consequences of building the bridge (low loss) were neither compelling nor convincing enough to warrant changing the Comprehensive Plan. On multiple occasions prior to the hearing Mr. Fields had publicly stated that he had no plans for the actual development of his property. He wanted to build the bridge in order to make it easier to sell it for a higher profit. Accordingly, most of the key assumptions underlying the Fields team's rationale for setting aside Goal Five provisions were based upon pure speculation.

In the end, this last argument carried the day. The burden of proof was on the applicant to make a convincing case that the project's benefits outweighed any of its foreseeable negative consequences. The commissioners were unanimous in rejecting the proposal. "I'm being asked to make a decision based on an assumption, based on a hypothetical," said one of them during the deliberative stage of the proceedings.

---

77 Narrative Demonstrating Compliance with 18.775.130 / ESEE documents on file at city of Tigard.

Many people who had come to the meeting to oppose the amendment went home giddy with success that night. But the veteran Watershed Folk stressed that the hearing had only been round one of what might become a long, drawn-out affair. Even though the Planning Commission had rejected the proposal, it would still get a hearing before the City Council, which could very well overrule the commission. Wait and see, they advised, and be prepared to make your case before the City Council if and when the opportunity arose.

How right they were. Even before the day of the hearing, the Fields team had been studying the merits of what they called "the Flex Option," a slightly longer and more expensive bridge design that was curved in such a way that it would skirt the wetlands by the slimmest of margins. Removing that pesky patch of sensitive land from the table would greatly facilitate their efforts to gain the necessary permits for the bridge. In less than a month they had the new plan in front of a hearings officer, and not long after that he determined that the new design no longer conflicted with the "sensitive lands" provision of the building code. With the wetlands off the table it was no longer necessary for the Fields team to seek an amendment to the city's Comprehensive Plan.

Since most arguments against the bridge had focused on its environmental impacts, the hearings officer's decision neutralized the majority of them as well. Only a handful of the folks who had attended the first meeting showed up for the last one. Because amending the code was no longer an issue, this meeting was closed to public testimony; so the few of us in opposition had to sit by somberly while the Planning Commission revisited the revised application. They quickly moved it through the deliberative process and were unanimous in their recommendation to approve the application. What the City Council would do with it in their turn was anyone's guess, but in any event the backbone of the resistance to the bridge appeared to have been broken.

As I left that last meeting I found myself reflecting on one of the most fundamental principles of local government: You can't fight City Hall. You could push, prod, advise, manipulate, even coerce; but in the end the best you could ever hope for was some kind of compromise. In most contexts compromise is a good thing; but as far as I was concerned, Fanno Creek had already been "compromised" half to death. Furthermore, somewhere in the process I had reached the conclusion that I possessed neither the intellectual skills nor the necessary patience to advocate effectively before commissions, councils or any other group in charge of governing the watershed. I couldn't discuss the issues without becoming angry. And no emotion is less effective in such settings than anger.

I sat in the truck for a while and thought about the body of law and custom currently governing the watershed. For months I had been wading through Tigard's comprehensive planning documents, code requirements, handbooks, Geological Information Systems files, maps and you-name-it. As a sort of intellectual triage I had tried to focus exclusively on the city and its issues. But in the end almost every scrap of information I gathered referred, directly or inferentially, to another source and to all kinds of side issues. It was research of a kind and on a level I had never attempted before, and quite candidly, I hated it. The worst day spent mucking around in the creek or talking with one of the Watershed Folk was a thousand times better than the best hour of grinding away at the seemingly bottomless wells of government documentation. I'd had enough, at least for a while.

The next day I called Sue Manning at Fowler Middle School and asked what was going on over in her neck of the woods.

"Come on over!" she exclaimed. "We're just getting ready to release another batch of salmon into Summer Creek. You'll have a ton of fun!"

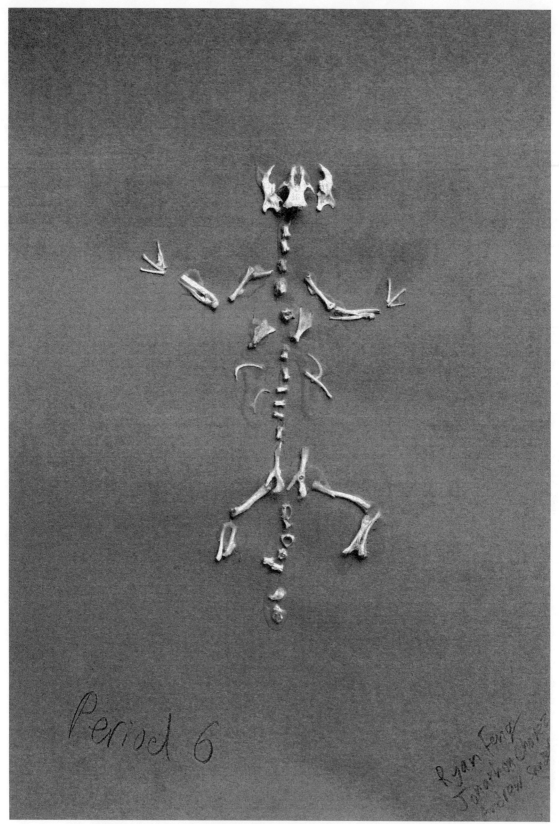

Bones of a small mammal teased from a bundle of owl vomit by Fowler Middle School students

6—A Little Education

Señor Hutsell's Trail

Gary Hutsell was a teacher at Fowler Middle School from 1984 to 2002. He taught Spanish and English as a Second Language, and he coached the girls' basketball team. He was popular with his students and colleagues. He loved to teach even more than he loved to fish, and he really loved to fish. One day Gary wasn't feeling well. He was rarely ill and even more rarely missed work, but something moved him to see a doctor. The doctor sent him to other doctors who did a bunch of tests. The results were bad, very bad. Gary had cancer of the brain, an inoperable tumor. On Saturday, May 31, 2002, only a few months after his first visit to the doctor, Gary Hutsell died.

I never knew the man, but I have a small black-and-white photograph of him propped up next to me as I write this. He is very near the end of his life in the photo, and he's sitting in a wooden chair by a small stream, fishing. He could not return to the classroom in those last days, but at least he could sit by a stream and take in some fresh air. From a photographic perspective the image is fairly degraded; but even without knowing that the man in the chair was close to the end of his days, anyone can see that there's a power in the image that is hard to explain rationally.

The scene was brightly lit by sunlight and the contrast is so extreme that the shadows are a solid black. The angle isn't all that good, either. The photographer was standing slightly behind Gary's left shoulder, too far away to capture more than a hint of his facial expression. In fact, all that is clearly delineated in the photo is the attitude of his seated profile. But even though you can't see much of his face, you can sense in the lean of the torso and the angle of the head an intense involvement with the moment. The image is filled with light, highly diffused light, scattering everywhere. Sitting there in the brightness, he looks to be more deeply involved in living than engaged in the dreary business of dying. I cannot look at the picture without wishing I had known him.

Gary's death hit the Fowler community very hard. It's a good-sized school of well over a thousand people, including students, staff and faculty; but it isn't so large that the sudden death of someone as popular and well-known as Gary could occur without considerable impact. As students and colleagues grappled with the grieving process, they cast about for a proper memorial, something that might express his contribution to the community in a concrete and self-perpetuating way. From the beginning everyone knew that whatever the memorial might be, it had to reflect the ultimate triumph of life over death if it were to have any chance of representing the essence of Gary's personality. Working from such a starting point it was almost inevitable that the school would end up linking his memory directly to a particular place on the campus.[78] Science teacher Mary Sue Scheller and her students were already hard at work developing an interpretive nature trail through the woods just across Spring Creek from the Fowler. The idea of turning the project into a memorial for Gary was quickly embraced by students and faculty alike. They turned their grief into hard work on a common cause and in the process began to heal their hearts.

Almost exactly a year after Gary's death, his passing was commemorated with the formal opening of Señor Hutsell's Trail. In addition to the students and Gary's immediate relatives, the mayor, members of the City Council, and members of various watershed organizations were in attendance. By everyone's account it was a wonderful event. The weather was especially good, even by May standards, and while the entire dedication was conducted with an air of solemnity, there were many smiles and also a fair amount of laughter. While working on the trail one of the students had found a piece of bark that bore a strong resemblance to a salmon, the well-known object of Gary's favorite pastime. Near the end of the ceremonies the student made a special presentation of the found-object to Gary's daughter.

The head of the nature trail is located just behind the school, at the northwest corner of a foot bridge spanning Summer Creek. There's a natural opening in the forest here, and with a single step into the interior a visitor is instantly surrounded by the substantial trunks of Douglas firs and western red cedars that have flanked Summer Creek for close to a century. From this starting point the trail meanders west along the north shore of the creek for over a quarter of a mile, then turns north and then east as it loops back to the main entrance. Numbered posts have been driven deep into the ground at 15 distinct points along the pathway. Each number corresponds to a notation in the nature guide that the students produced for the memorial. While some of the students channeled their love for Hutsell and their grief over his passing into the development of the nature trail, others invested theirs in the production of the guide. The students researched plant species, produced signage and wrote the text. The brochure is printed in English and Spanish and explains the focus of 15 highlights that can be found along the trail today. More than two dozen well-rendered depictions of the many species of native plant life found along the trail adorn the page margins—corn lily, vine maple, western red cedar, Douglas fir and salal, to name just a few. Here's a typical entry:

78 The campus occupies approximately 25 acres of land that includes almost a mile-long section of Summer Creek. Much of the property is covered with stands of ponderosa pine, Douglas fir, western red-cedar, big leaf maple and Oregon ash. It is adjacent to 43 acres of similar property recently acquired by Tigard (with financial assistance from the Trust for Public Land and Oregon Watershed Enhancement Board). The property will be developed as parkland.

Stop 9, The Woodpecker Tree: This western red cedar is a favorite in our forest for the pileated woodpecker. It is the only woodpecker in our area that makes oval or rectangular holes. If you look closely you can see where another type of bird has made a nest in one of the holes left by the woodpecker.

For more than half its length the trail follows the meandering creek and then winds through some of Tigard's richest natural resources. In a surprisingly short distance the trail passes over terrain as varied as the vegetation that flourishes on it. Near the creek it is swampy and filled with herbaceous plants and wetland shrubs. The banks rise steeply along the north bank and top out at twenty feet above the creek's floodplain. This upland area also contains a few springs, and in the wet season large portions of the northwestern end become wetlands of their own.

In addition to its varied terrain, the undeveloped portions of the property contain some of the most diverse and important ecosystem resources in the entire Fanno Creek watershed. The canopy includes ponderosa pine, Douglas fir, western red cedar, big leaf maple, Oregon ash, and native oak. The understory is equally diverse and features an abundance of woody and herbaceous plants native to the Pacific Northwest. In early spring large areas of the forest floor are covered in dense patches of trillium, followed shortly thereafter by equally dense patches of camas. The waterfowl and small game commonly found around the rest of the watershed are plentiful in this area as well. Wood duck and pileated woodpeckers nest here. Sightings of beaver are common and—rarest of the rare—otter and western painted turtle have been spotted in this area by reliable witnesses on more than one occasion. As one of the Watershed Folk recently put it, this small watershed is "the jewel" in Tigard's natural resources crown.

The bulk of the 30-acre Fowler campus lies on the south side of Summer Creek. Facilities consist of the main school building, a small outbuilding, a baseball diamond and an Olympic-sized oval track. The entrance to the trail is directly across the creek from the schoolhouse and just a couple of hundred yards by sidewalk and hardened pathways from the back doors of the science classrooms. This makes it possible for the science faculty and their students to move to and from the trail area without leaving muddy footprints all up and down the main corridors of the school.

Given the quality of this acreage and its proximity to the classrooms, it is not surprising that the science faculty utilize the area as a direct extension of the classroom. The curriculum for the three grade levels at Fowler includes a strong emphasis on all the sciences, and the wetlands and uplands nearby provide a treasure trove of supplemental material. But using such resources as part of the curriculum for course work at any level is far more complex and difficult than it may first appear, particularly given the requirements, standards and practices of contemporary education. Managing students in the open woods takes a rare breed of teacher, someone one with the eyes of a hawk, the resourcefulness of a raccoon and the patience of a snake.

Sue Manning

I opened the front door of the school and was enveloped by the smell of children. "What is it about that odor?" I muttered to myself as I left the reception area and headed for Sue Manning's classroom. Certain scents, especially ones deeply linked with some defining circumstance, are teleportals to earlier days. So it is for me with the interior spaces of a middle school, where the pronounced muskiness of puberty somehow manages to make its way through the strange blend of other odors: cafeteria food, unwashed bodies, mildewed carpets and department store perfumes.

A couple of sixth graders zipped past me, late to class and trying to laugh it off. Was I really that young when I took Julia L. into the deserted band master's office, swore that I loved her more than Virginia P. and then kissed her full on the mouth? She had tasted like sweet but slightly soured milk. Still holding that long-ago moment in my mind, I reached for the door handle to Sue's classroom, only to see it swing open in front of me. I recoiled, fully expecting for a split second to see, once again, the startled face of the band master as he opened the door on Julia and me in mid-kiss. But it was Sue Manning; unlike the band master, she was glad to see me standing there all red-faced and rattled.

"Oh, there you are," she said. "I was just coming to get you. I'm on my way to pick up rain coats and you're just in time to help out! Oh, and check these out when we get back." She pointed to a dozen or so 5 by 7-inch pieces of colored construction paper tacked to the wall just outside the door. Each one displayed the reassembled skeletons of small rodents. "The kids did these for their barn owl project. Aren't they great? They sort through owl pellets until they've retrieved as many of the prey animal's bones as possible, and then they reconstruct the skeletons as part of an anatomy lesson. Cool, huh?"

There was something comical yet touching in these artless constructions, a directness of thought and action somehow very satisfying to observe. What kind of mind comes up with this stuff, I wondered? This particular science project is so popular with teachers that a small but thriving industry in owl vomit has developed to support it.

Sue's classroom would make a great movie set, I decided, as my eye roamed the space. It was filled to capacity with shelves, cabinets, sinks, posters, aquariums, cages, animal artifacts, kites, bird houses, audio-visual equipment, computers, display cases and file cabinets. In the rear of the classroom stood a large wheeled rack holding 24 pairs of black rubber boots with red soles. Another half dozen were lined up near the door. Next to the boot-cart was a long table covered with dozens of garden gloves and rain coats, gear that would be worn later in the period when Sue took the students outside to begin work on the major science project for the term.

All this gear showed signs of recent and heavy use. But, like the classroom itself, it was relatively clean and well maintained. Against the back wall and adjacent to a small computer station sat a fifty-gallon aquarium atop a cabinet that housed a variety of related equipment, including a pump-filter-cooler rig that delivered a steady supply of chilled water to the several hundred salmon eggs that would soon hatch into tiny Chinook fry. A few feet away stood a large bird cage on a rolling cart. Inside, a quartet of zebra finches chirped away, a sound that quickly merged into the background sounds of the classroom—the bubbling of the aquarium and the deep hum of its pump; the HVAC unit in the ceiling above humming at a still deeper level; kids coming into class, moving chairs and settling in. There was plenty of noise but the room was not particularly noisy. Kind of like the sound ducks make when a flock of them are feeding on a pond, I decided after a minute or two of reflection.

There was a sense of comfort to the place, a feeling of well-established routines, an atmosphere almost entirely devoid of tension; "measured" was the word that came to mind. Sue had only been with this batch of seventh graders for just over a month, but by now most of them were on auto-pilot as far as basic classroom protocols were concerned. There were 28 of them in the room that morning, and I reflected on the skill sets required just to control such a group, much less teach them anything.

Sue laughed when I asked how she managed it. "Never show your fear." Then more seriously, "I spend most of the first week or two focused on establishing a comfortable space for them. I keep the projects fun and focus on easily-reached, positive goals. It's mostly about developing trust. Not much in the way of learning will happen with kids on this level until they trust you."

I pressed her for a more concrete recipe. "What exactly does it take to establish trust with middle schoolers?" I asked.

She thought for a moment. "Pretty much the same thing it takes to establish trust with anyone," she said. "Predictability, fairness, honesty. It helps a lot if they know you really like kids and are prepared to accept them for what they are. You can't be phony about any of this. Individually they might be fooled for a while, but collectively, somehow, they can spot a phony a mile away."

Building Bioswales

I first met Sue after a friend of mine told me about the bioswales she and her students were building in the parking lot at Fowler Middle School. "Rain gardens," she called them, and she was using them to help the students learn the basics of bio-filtration and related eco-site development. Sue had led them through a series of units designed to help them understand how these kinds of structures can clean stormwater runoff and, at the same time, beautify an area. To augment this information Sue had recruited a few professionals from the field to come into the classroom and speak on topics particularly relevant to the project.

One of those speakers had been Brian Wegener of the Tualatin Riverkeepers, who gave an audio-visual presentation covering the key environmental issues associated with an urban watershed. Brian's presentation included graphic examples of how stormwater runoff impacts overall water quality in the Tualatin basin. It also detailed how stormwater retrofits, such as the rain gardens the students were working on, can help improve habitat and water quality in urbanized areas. Somehow, Brian was able to make even the more technical concepts accessible to the kids without dumbing-down the language or the content.

Another watershed professional, Lori Faha, had discussed the design and construction of bio filters and detailed the processes involved in their installation. Lori is an engineer and consultant, and for much of her early career she worked for the Unified Sewerage Agency, the organization that was ultimately reorganized into Clean Water Services. In 1997 she served as project manager for the development of the agency's first comprehensive Fanno Creek Watershed Management Plan, a document that led to the installation of some of the first bioswales in the watershed. In addition to providing classroom presentations, Lori was serving as "project engineer" for the rain garden project itself. In this capacity she would help Sue coordinate a variety of community resources, including technical and physical assistance from cws.

I had noticed one of those resources when I visited the school a few days earlier—a huge blue tanker truck with the Clean Water Services logo on its side. The men from this truck were pouring large amounts of water onto select areas of the parking lot, and Lori and the kids were mapping out the resultant flows. The basic plan was to redirect that flow so that it went through the long axis of each island, rather than around the curbs themselves. Earlier in the week Sue had taken a group of her students outside to the project area, where they measured the site's dimensions. Lori's team would incorporate those measurements with their own data and convert the results into a site map. Then the students would develop schematics of the site areas, including a large one for the whiteboard at the front of the room. When these schematics were finished,

Sue would make multiple copies for her classes so that everyone could get a better sense of what to expect when the actual project work began.

Once the actual flow characteristics of the areas involved were better understood, the students would be able to develop their own individual concept plans. A final design would be developed from these concept sketches. Sue had given me several to study while she tended to some pre-class chores. Like the reassembled rodent skeletons tacked up outside the classroom door, these plans possessed an artless but frank integrity that was quite captivating. I was deep into wondering whether or not a similar integrity was manifested in the work these kids did in their art classes when Sue's amplified voice broke the spell.

She quickly laid out the program for the next hour of class, provided a couple of students with specific chores and then directed the group to the back of the room, where they began donning rubber boots and rain jackets. There are three doors to Sue's classroom—one that leads back into the school, one that connects this room with another much like it, and a third that opens up on the north or backside of the building. The kids streamed outside through this third door and headed for a nearby shed where shovels, buckets and other gear were stored.

I looked at my watch. We had just over half an hour before the students would need to be back in the classroom, out of their boots and slickers, and ready to go to their next class. During that brief time they would need to complete several tasks critical to the overall success of the term's major science project. Sue had told me earlier that she was apprehensive about this project. "It's a little like the students themselves: lots of moving parts that can quickly get out of control if you're not always in command," she had said.

Partly in order to achieve as many objectives as possible and partly to ensure that none of the kids ended up just standing around, Sue had assigned each group to a particular task. One group would dig holes at the two sites for "perk" or infiltration tests; another would verify site measurements to ensure that the master site plan was as accurate as possible. A third group was put to work pulling ivy from the trees lining the south side of the parking lot.

A parent volunteer had been scheduled to assist, but when she didn't materialize, Sue asked me to work with the diggers. Four perk holes would need digging, two on each of the traffic islands, and it quickly became obvious that it would take serious muscle to reach a depth sufficient to make test results reliable. The top three or four inches of grass and soil were easily removed, but just an inch or so further down the ground was hardpan.

A perk test (short for percolation) is a simple method of determining the degree to which water can be absorbed at a given site. When skillfully employed, the method can yield a fairly precise measurement of the soil's permeability. First, a hole about a foot in diameter and one to two feet deep is dug into the surface and then filled with water. This first fill is designed to saturate the materials in the hole. Once the water has been completely absorbed by the surrounding medium, about a cubic foot of fresh water is poured into the hole. The rate at which this volume subsides is measured at intervals over a given time span, usually not more than thirty minutes to an hour, which in turn yields a calculation of drain time per cubic foot. Such calculations are useful in the installation of septic tanks and related drainfields, and equally useful in the design and construction of bioswales.

While the kids and I labored away at the perk holes, a smaller group focused on making the final site survey. They worked in teams of two, one to run the hundred-foot-long survey tape and the other to record data. Lori Faha helped them select their reference points, explaining how the process of flooding the parking lot was used to calculate runoff rates and slope characteristics. The crew from cws had painted blue lines on the high and low sides of the curbing, indicating where it would need to be breached to maximize the volume of stormwater that would flow through the completed bioswale. Lori noted that, in addition to the proposed apertures in the curb, it would be necessary to build a couple of low risers—speed bumps, essentially—across two portions of the parking area to redirect runoff into the bioswales. With her guidance, the survey crews incorporated these inputs into their revisions of the master site plan.

Meanwhile, the third group had tackled the ivy pulling task with real gusto. From personal experience I knew that there is something wonderfully cathartic about gripping and ripping ivy vines off of tree trunks and out of the dirt at the base of trees. The kids had caught on to this, and were going at it like heroes when Sue finally blew the whistle, stopping all activity. Back in the classroom, she made a few final comments, explained the next steps and somehow managed to wrap up the entire process just as the bell rang.

Sue ran through the same process with several more classes that day, and by the time the last group assembled on the site there wasn't much for them to do but fill the perk holes and pack up the digging tools. The enthusiasm of the various teams of diggers had resulted in four holes, each well over two feet deep and equally wide, at least at the top. These were filled with water as rapidly as possible, and then everyone began cleaning up the area. Once again, I was surprised at how orderly and relaxed the process was. After the last students had put their chairs on the tables and left for the day, Sue and I sat down for a short postmortem. I asked how she felt about the day's progress.

"Well," she said, after a short pause, "I'm not happy with the crappy soil we've encountered. Did you notice that the water level in the holes wasn't going down *at all*?[79] That means cws will have to increase the amount of good dirt

---

79 The holes never drained. CWS filled them up a couple of weeks later when they graded the areas and then covered them with at least six inches of pretty good dirt.

they add to the area after they've dug out the channels. If they simply put the stuff they dig out back in, then these things will become wading pools rather than water treatment facilities." She rolled her eyes. "That would not be a good thing. Other than that, though, everything went great. The kids were especially on task today, and we got more accomplished than I had originally hoped for. Aren't they the best?

"They're really into this project, maybe more than any of the others we've worked on before. At the beginning, I brought them out to the parking lot and showed them how the water from these lots was going into a big pipe that carries it across the campus and empties it directly into the stream. They were really shocked and disappointed. I think that might have been the first time that most of them ever really looked at how the water around them gets dealt with. Intuitively, they understood that it just isn't right, and they immediately wanted to do something about it. I'm very proud of them."

"What about learning?" I asked. "What do you think the kids actually learned today?"

"Probably the most important thing they learned today was that plans and designs have to be cross-checked against reality. That's what this whole session was mostly about. We had covered a lot of this material in the classroom, particularly the part about infiltration (the perk tests). We even made a theoretical calculation of how much additional topsoil cws would have to bring in to make these gardens actually work as bioswales. What we found out today is that the information on soils we used to estimate infiltration rates didn't apply to the areas we're working on. During the next class or two we'll discuss that finding, as well as some errors we found in our original site measurements, and then we'll draw up an improved plan. We did pretty much the same thing after the flow test last week—checked theory against the real world."

We went on to talk about what a great tool this kind of project can be when it comes to teaching subject matter that can be too dry for many learners if an immediate application of the process is not possible. Sue emphasized that mathematical and physical concepts have a visceral basis that is hard to experience in the classroom. But the planning and design work involved in creating a bioswale can engage adolescents on a level that ordinary mathematical exercises can't. If the conceptual work is a prelude to the physical process of actually constructing the facility—digging, grading, planting and maintenance, for example—the learning is amplified and reinforced.

Sue's bioswale project occupied most of the first semester of the 2007–2008 school year. Design and planning activities consumed the first month, while site preparations and planting activities dominated the balance of the semester. The actual groundbreaking took place in early November. Lori Faha

Sue Manning teaching a lesson on the mysterious nature of owls

supervised the students as they used cans of white spray paint to indicate the shapes and elevations of the swales. Then personnel and equipment from cws began excavating the designated areas.

A week later, on an unseasonably sunny and warm Monday, another group of cws personnel arrived to help the students place hundreds of native plants into the soil. Although on this occasion several parents showed up to help, it was a day-long process and the cws crew didn't leave until well into the evening. I stopped by the school a few days later and walked the site with Sue. She was pleased with everything, particularly the assistance the cwspersonnel had provided. "Above and beyond," she noted. But she was also clearly worried about something. I pressed her for a reason.

"I'm just concerned about this summer," she confessed. "Ordinarily, these kinds of sites have a sprinkler system built into them so they can be kept wet during the dry summer months for the first few years. All the species we planted are natives and drought resistant, but most of them need time to put roots down before they can be left entirely to fend for themselves. We didn't have the resources for a sprinkler system, so I'm trying to work out a deal with the grounds crew that'll be tending the place this summer. But I'm not sure, given our current budget issues, that the crew will even be here. It's very worrisome."

I understood her concern. It can take two to three years for the vegetation used in bioswales to establish itself. During that time it is highly vulnerable to the long dry spell that typically occurs between July and August. Many well-intentioned restorations have failed because of the relatively harsh summer conditions here in the Northwest.

"I'm also very worried about our salmon tank," Sue went on." I'm not sure the thermostat is working properly, and the eggs will be arriving any day now."

"Salmon eggs?" I was intrigued.

"Yeah, the last couple of years we've been rearing and releasing spring-run Chinook into Summer Creek. To some extent, that's what led to the idea of making rain gardens in the parking lot. The water from the lot flows directly into the spot where we release the little ones. There are already salmonids in the stream—cutthroat trout. It's an extremely long shot, but we hope that someday the creek might support a population of spring-run Chinook. We release them just below the foot bridge that leads to Señor Hutsell's Trail. You should be here when we release them," Sue added. "It's a ton of fun!"

Snow Ball

On the way home that day I reflected on how Sue had tied the indoor and outdoor classrooms together. So far that semester, she had guided her students through a wide variety of topics specific to the natural sciences. While she used multiple teaching strategies, almost all of them had involved the direct application of basic math and science principles to concrete events of a more qualitative nature. It had been a semester focused on multiple "-ologies," each presented initially as stand-alone disciplines, then quickly integrated into the execution of a handful of major projects. Ecology, biology, geology, hydrology— the list went on and on. Indoor work had dominated the agenda, of course, but each lesson was usually focused on the world immediately outside the doors of the building. Observation, measurement, analysis, assessment and direct action had been involved in every project, from the dissection of owl pellets in the classroom to creation of a fully functioning wetlands in the parking lot.

There was no question in my mind that Sue was taking her students well into what Richard Louv[80] describes as the Fourth Frontier. "Wonderland," he calls it, a place where the young are repatriated with the land; a place where the fear of potential liabilities has ceased to handcuff faculty and school administrators; a place where our cultural norms support, rather than thwart, a deeper physical and spiritual relationship with the natural world. I was also convinced that she was doing a great job of it.

Part of that impression had developed from observing how the children tended to approach their activities and their classmates during her lessons. They appeared to be so *comfortable* with things and with each other. There was, in both the gait of their walk and their manner of standing close together, an expression of the kind of intimacy, or at least the easy familiarity you might ordinarily associate with members of a well-coached sports team. Then it dawned on me. These kids were living in the essence of community. They were learning how to respect the land and in the process were learning how to respect each other.

A few weeks later Sue called. "If you want to get some shots of the kids releasing their fish into Summer Creek, you need to come by tomorrow." I had been looking forward to this moment for quite some time. While spring-run Chinook salmon were not historically present in the Fanno Creek system, other salmonids were. Cutthroat trout and steelhead used to spawn in the lower reaches of Fanno Creek until siltification and other forms of pollution too numerous to mention rendered the waterways uninhabitable. Occasionally a few stray Cohos would stick their heads in as well. Summer Creek was a favored spot because the stream is spring-fed and once was icy cold for most of the year. Most of that stream quality has been lost to the waves of agricultural and commercial development that have swept through the area over the last hundred years. A great deal of restoration has taken place along many reaches of the creek, so conditions have improved greatly in the last few decades. Temper-

80 Louv (2005)

ature remains a major problem, however, because the main stem of the stream is blocked by numerous dams. Still, efforts to reestablish breeding populations of salmon continue. ODFW provides the fry, along with the necessary equipment and technical support, while the faculty and students at Fowler do the rest.

I arrived early the next morning. Sue is partial to mochas so I'd picked up a grande for her on my way in. "What's the battle plan?" I asked.

"Pretty simple," she replied. "Each kid gets a single fish in one of these plastic cups. Then we all head out the back door, go down to the creek and dump them in. We're lucky today because it's been pretty dry and the banks aren't too slippery. We may get by without having to haul anyone out of the stream."

Students began arriving and Sue turned her attention to them. I had been around this particular group often enough that they took my presence in stride. I settled down at the back of the room, a spot that would allow me to get a shot or two of Sue dishing out fish when the time came. This was a big day, so I had anticipated a little more craziness from the kids than appeared to be forthcoming. The energy level in the room didn't begin to go up until Sue got around to explaining the procedures that would be used for the day's activity. She had already determined the order in which the children would collect their individual fish, so the subsequent procession to and from the tank was very orderly, albeit a bit noisy. The plan was for everyone to head for the creek at roughly the same time, so those who had already had scored a fish (in some cases two fish!) had a chance to mingle and compare notes. Standing there with their little plastic cups and talking casually to each other, they looked like adults at a cocktail party.

When the last student had received her fish, the door opened and the group began a slow and orderly procession to the bridge over Summer Creek, only a couple of hundred yards from Sue's classroom. En route, I joined a trio of boys who were having a great time and asked the obvious ringleader the name of his fish.

During the quarter, as the students had worked on the projects and lessons that supported the release, Sue had required them to draw a picture of the fish they hoped to receive, then give it a name. She had debated with herself whether or not to do this. As a scientist and naturalist, she is very conscious of the issues that can arise whenever we anthropomorphize nature. In the end she convinced herself that the potentially negative aspects of the fish portrait assignment were outweighed by the benefits that accrue when people are able to relate more directly to any living thing.

The kid held out his cup and grinned. "This is Snow Ball. Isn't she a beaut?"

Snow Ball, I remembered, was the name of the crippled doe that had caused such a stir in these parts earlier in the year. Now, as I watched the kid's tiny fish wriggle in the cup, I thought about that incident and the public relations

One of Sue Manning's students watching as his Chinook fry swims to freedom

disaster it had been for ODFW. The media pushed the story so hard back then that you couldn't turn on the radio or the TV without hearing about it. Naturally enough, I assumed that the deer had been the source of this young man's inspiration.

"Yes," I allowed, "she's gorgeous. But what made you name her after that deer?"

"Deer? I didn't name her after no deer. That's just the chance in hell she has of ever making it back to this bridge."

I related the story to Sue when I joined her on the bridge. She laughed, said she knew exactly who it was I had been speaking to, then returned to watching over the other children as they took their cups to different places along the banks and began releasing their fish into the creek. Just beneath the bridge a log about two feet in diameter protruded into the center of the stream. It was a piece of "big wood," placed there by Clean Water Services when they had restored this stretch of embankment a few years earlier. Its butt-end was buried deeply into the embankment. A boy dressed entirely in black came down the steep slope carrying his cup well away from his body. He wore a heavy sweatshirt whose long sleeves were adorned with colorful renditions of serpents and deaths-heads. His fingernails were painted black, and his long, chestnut hair was carefully uncombed. Without a moment's hesitation he walked out onto the log until he was well away from the bank.

I looked at Sue and raised my eyebrows.

"He'll be fine," she said, although she didn't take her eyes off him for an instant. "Even if he does fall in, the water is less than three feet deep in that spot. And he won't fall in. They hardly ever do, and when it does happen it's almost always on purpose. But this is December and they'll do everything they can to stay high and dry."

With infinite care the kid splashed a few drops of creek water into the cup, swirled it around gently and then then studied the effect. After repeating this process a few times, he finally began lowering the cup into the water, tilting it forward until the stream entered and took away the fish. I was too far away to see the fish actually pass over the lip and into the stream, but I knew exactly the moment it happened. Everything in the subtle change of the young man's posture communicated the event. He continued to crouch on the log for several more moments before finally making his way back to shore. Was he savoring the moment, I wondered? I surely was.

"Wow! That was great to watch," I said to Sue. "That one most definitely has a chance of making it, don't you think?"

"Yes," she said, after reflecting a moment. "And the fish might just make it, as well."

Warren and Al looking for "floaters" near the mouth of Fanno Creek

7—A Line In The Mud

Big Blue

The heron came in low and fast, not more than a few feet above the tangle of fallen saplings that for the moment served as my blind. It settled somewhere on the opposite shoreline, out of sight but less than a hundred yards away. I waited a few dozen heartbeats, then began crawling through the brush-pile that lay between us, plowing along through the soggy detritus, sometimes on my hands and knees, but mostly on my belly. The funky stink of mud and rotting vegetation filled my lungs. I stopped for a moment and rose up on one elbow to get my bearings, then froze in mid-motion. The bird was just across the creek, perched on an old ash deadfall that hung out over the water. I had made no sound, I was sure of it, but his head whipped around and suddenly he was staring directly into my eyes. A tiny rivulet of rain water began working its way under my collar, trickled across bare skin and ran down the inside of my armpit and across my ribs. The brim of my sodden Tilley hat was festooned with raindrops. They jiggled with every breath. I focused on this chandelier and concentrated on holding its tiny, twinkling rainbows as still as possible.

From a photographic standpoint the situation was hopeless. The tangle of trunks and limbs above my prostrate body made an effective blind, but would also prevent me from getting a clean shot. The instant I raised my camera the heron would be sure to see me, and that would be that. Even with the motor-drive on, I'd be lucky to get one clean shot before he vanished. I was just beginning to coil myself up for a final lunge out of the brush pile when, out of nowhere, a troop of kinglets showed up. Had I dared move at all I could have easily reached out and touched a couple of them.

In my world a close-up encounter with kinglets in the woods is a propitious event, a sign that things are going to be all right, no matter what those "things" may be. These were golden-crowned kinglets and as usual they were in the company of chickadees. There were other birds in the group as well, juncos for sure, if my hearing wasn't off. I resisted turning my head to look, for fear of breaking the spell. They were feeding on something in the moss-coated bark covering my blind. Aphids, I speculated, as one of the tiny birds worked its way along the branch directly in front of my face. Suddenly it was hanging upside down, not a foot away from my face. I didn't blink but I might have grinned. *Zee-Zee-Zee* it buzzed, and along with the rest of its tribe was off like a shot. As they and their high-pitched racket fled the area, Big Blue swooshed its giant wings and rose to go as well. I got off one shot before it vanished beyond the tree tops.

I shifted to a sitting position and pulled a small thermos of coffee out of my pack. There was a package of cheese and peanut butter crackers in there as well. My muddy hands smelled like they'd been in a sack of mushrooms. The water-proofing in the seat of my well-worn rain suit had failed to such an extent that my buttocks were as damp as they were numb. It had been almost thirty years since I'd last had a cigarette, but for a brief instant I craved one. I brushed a piece of dirty moss off the last cracker, wolfed it down and sealed the deal with the last swig of tepid coffee. It began to rain again. Gary Snyder[81] had been closer to the truth than maybe even he understood: you don't really enter the watershed until you've crawled through it on your belly for a hundred yards or so, dragging its little treasures along with you as you go.

The consequence of too much coffee suddenly caught up with me and ruined the reverie. Time to go. I worked my way through a patch of dead blackberries and back onto the trail. I couldn't see the creek, but I knew from many previous visits to this quiet place that its sinuous body was only a few yards away in almost any direction. I was walking down the long axis of an emerging oxbow.

A short distance down the trail I reached the end of the oxbow. In this place the creek's cradle is 12 feet deep and five times that wide. Damp as it had been for days, the actual rainfall still hadn't amounted to much. The creek itself wasn't more than thigh-deep. It wasn't bearing a great deal of sediment either; I could make out the rocky bottom quite clearly. The current was strong and steady but wasn't displaying the sense of urgency it shows during heavy rain events. There are many days out of the year when this entire stretch of channel is filled to the brim with a frothy, brown, undulating flood. At least a couple times a year the stream overtops these banks and spreads out through the underbrush. I glanced around, looking for the telltale signs of a recent flood event. There they were, phalanxes of dead reed canary grass flattened to the ground, all pointing, in their water-combed way, towards the Fanno-Tualatin confluence less than a tenth of a mile away.

How many times have I come here since 2007, I wondered? A couple dozen, for sure. "Here" was a place near the end of the last mile of meanders Fanno Creek makes before emptying into the Tualatin River. I got my first full-body dunking in the creek at this spot and tasted my first mouthful of its water in the process. Earthy and green it had been, and I spent the next eight hours in suspense, waiting to see if I had ingested any giardia. This is also where I saw my first good-sized fish, a cutthroat trout as near as I could tell from the brief study I was able to give it before it sped into the deep pool just upstream. And on a gray and rainy spring morning in 2009, this is where I learned about the mysterious ways of the freshwater mussel.

81 Snyder (1995)

Comrades in Arms

Al and Warren have known each other for fifty years. They met in the early 1960s, when Al was still in college and working as a seasonal employee with ODFW. Warren had already been with the agency long enough to be a project leader. While their career paths with ODFW soon went in different directions, they've managed to maintain close contact with each other for most of that time. In their combined careers with the agency, these two men logged in almost a century of service, much which was spent out in the field. They came on board when the agency's role was fairly simple: keep the state's lands full of game and its waters full of fish. By the time they retired from ODFW its mission hadn't changed all that much, but actually achieving it had become considerably more complex.

"Was it politics that changed it so much, do you think?" I addressed Warren's broad back one day as we walked single file down a narrow path in the woods.

"Not really," he replied. "Oh, the politics are certainly complex and sometimes very annoying. But really, a lot of the complexity comes from us just knowing so much more about the science of it all. We not only have better information these days, but better ways of dealing with it as well."

I could see Al nodding his head as he walked point through some blackberries bordering the creek bank. "That's true," he said. "And a lot of the complexity comes from having to manage so much more of the overall process." We had reached the streambed by now, and as Al made ready to wade in and start looking for mussels, I asked him to elaborate.

"Well, take conservation for example," he explained. "The agency has always had a strong conservation mission, but because we're dealing with such a beat-up environment these days, pushing that portion of the agency's work has become a lot more urgent and critical. Habitat is everything, and since it's under such constant pressure we have to find new ways of maximizing our efforts to maintain and protect what's left."

He had waded into the stream and was already peering down into the water with his viewing scope. The scope eliminates surface glare, making it possible to see through water almost as if it were air. I'd made a similar device many years ago out of a couple of feet of spare six-inch PVC pipe, but it was nowhere near as sophisticated and effective as Al's commercially produced viewer. It featured a tilted interior lens that made it possible to look through the device without having to pull it completely up to your face. I made a note to order one from the same company as soon as I got home that night.[82]

Al's knowledge of mussels and other macro-invertebrates is encyclopedic, and he is one of the most well-known scientists in the region. While he

82 http://www.watermonitoringequip.com/pages/lake.html

searched the stream bottom for mussels, Warren and I splashed along a short distance behind. It was May and the vegetation along the bank created a near-ly impenetrable screen between the creek and the surrounding woods. It also eliminated a great deal of the background noise that otherwise tends to dimin-ish the aesthetic experience of being in this portion of the watershed. As we waded upstream through the green corridor, Warren talked about his wildlife work with ODFW. Most of it had taken place on the east side of the Cascades, and he was particularly familiar with the Lower Deschutes and Northeastern Oregon watersheds. His primary area of interest had been wildlife manage-ment, and for half of his career the game and fish commissions were separate entities.[83] The Service had been ahead of its time in a lot of ways, he noted, and asked me if I knew that ODFW was one of the first agencies of its type to use a decentralized approach to fish and game management. Did I know that it was also one of the first to use district biologists to support those regions?

I confessed that I knew next to nothing about the agency other than its mis-sion of protecting and managing wildlife around the state. I had never really thought about its role in the management of urban wildlife until I attended a conference focused on beaver management a year earlier. I went because I hoped to learn more about the management issues associated with urban bea-ver. The meeting had been informative in some ways, but I was left with the distinct impression that urban beaver populations were hardly a blip on the agency's radar. Later, a mutual friend introduced me to Warren, and I soon learned that not only had he attended the same meeting but he had come away with a similar set of concerns.

Warren lives a block from a place on Ash Creek where beaver have created one of the longest dams in the Fanno Creek watershed. The dam sits across a portion of Ash Creek that flows through Tigard, but just upstream the impound-ed waters have flooded more than an acre of private property. The waterlogged conditions have killed many of the large trees in the area. When he studied the jurisdictional issues involved, Warren had not been surprised to discover that considerable confusion exists over what can and can't be done to remedy these kinds of beaver-based problems.

"What struck me at the time," he said, as we continued up the creek, "was how complex beaver management issues are in urban areas. There are a tre-mendous number of jurisdictional layers you have to run through before you can find someone with anything like a final say in how a problem should be resolved. Even with all my years of field experience, I still don't fully have a handle on it."

Just then Al spoke up and suggested we move to another part of the stream.

83 In 1975 the Fish Commission (responsible for commercial fisheries) and the Wildlife Commission (re-sponsible for wildlife and game fisheries) merged and became the Oregon Department of Fish and Wildlife.

He had reached a hole too deep for him to tackle with his scope. So far he hadn't found a single mussel, but he wasn't particularly surprised or worried about their absence in this particular area. "I've never seen mussels in this reach, but it's always worth a look-see. Further upstream, for about a half-mile of the creek on either side of Scholls Ferry Road, I usually have no trouble finding them. My guess is that we're poking around a little too early in the year; but let's head upstream and see what we find."

Finding Floaters

Our quest that day had been to find a freshwater mussel.[84] Even one live specimen would do, as far as I was concerned. I already had a couple of shells that Al had shared with me, but I very much wanted to see one that was actually making its home somewhere along the bottom of Fanno Creek. These mussels are "excellent indicators of the long-term health of aquatic ecosystems."[85] For one thing, they are not particularly mobile, which means that their absence or presence—as well as their general condition when found—can tell you a great deal about the cumulative impacts of local conditions.

Freshwater mussels are sensitive to a number of critical water quality characteristics, including levels of dissolved oxygen, foreign chemicals and excessive levels of sedimentation. Since they are filter feeders and live in the mud along the bottom and banks of streams, analysis of their tissues can provide evidence of heavy metals and other contaminants that are harmful to most other living organisms in the ecosystem. Finally, a portion of their reproductive process depends upon the presence of fish in the environment. After fertilization, mussel eggs develop into free-floating larvae that must attach themselves to suitable host-fish before they can go on to the next step of their maturation process. Coho salmon have been identified as a host species for Oregon floaters, the species of mussel found in Fanno Creek, but other fish more commonly found there may also serve as hosts.

"I think the creek is in pretty good shape, comparatively," said Al. "You have to remember that just fifty years ago it was as good as dead. I almost always find plenty of mussel sign in various areas up and down the length of the creek these days. That's a strong indicator that at least key parts of the habitat are in good enough condition to support a solid population of cutthroat and steelhead. We know that they were here in abundance historically,[86] and we also know from fish surveys that they've continued to survive, in spite of all the pollution that used to be thrown at them."

84 The mussels are called "floaters" partly because their thin and light-weight shells allow them to "float" in the fine silt and partly because when they die they sometimes float on the surface of the water.
85 Smith (2009)
86 Xerxes Society (2012). So far only two species have been USFWS listed, neither of which are found in Oregon.

Warren agreed with Al. We happened to be standing in an area that had remained more or less intact for several decades. He motioned towards the creek and the dense stands of vegetation along its banks. "This place is never going to look like a virgin stream, and you might not even want it to. In this kind of climate a genuinely wild stream corridor would be an impenetrable jungle of fallen trees and dense underbrush. You'd be lucky if you could move more than three feet at a time, even if you were walking in the middle of the stream. But for being just a few thousand yards away from one of the biggest shopping malls in the area, it's a pretty natural environment."

He paused and examined the ground for a moment before continuing. "I don't see any tracks right here, but while we were walking upstream I saw plenty of deer and beaver sign, and maybe even an otter track or two. We've heard and seen all kinds of water fowl and other birds today and I suspect if we put our minds to it we could spot the nest that those red-tailed hawks have been bragging about for the last half hour." He laughed. "And if we really worked at it, we might catch a glimpse of one of those 'coyotees' you are always talking about. I'm pretty sure a pack of them police this place every night." [87]

When asked about the creek's greatest challenges, Al and Warren generally agreed about the biggest challenges facing the creek in the future, differing only in the emphasis each put on a specific issue: Chemical pollution, fragmentation, loss of habitat, erosion and water temperature were their top items. I nodded in agreement as they ticked them off, but something in my demeanor must have caught Warren's attention. "What do *you* think they are?" he asked.

I hesitated. I'd spoken up on this issue in the presence of other Watershed Folk a few times, and invariably they looked at me as if I was crazy. "I think the creek is dying," I said.

Sure enough, they both looked at me as if I was crazy.

"That's a little extreme, don't you think?" asked Al after a moment of silence. "I know we haven't found find any mussels today, but that doesn't mean they aren't here. I think the creek looks pretty good, particularly when you compare it to how polluted it was thirty years ago." Warren shook his head in mute agreement, but I pressed ahead anyway.

"It isn't dying because of pollution or anything like that. It's dying because its footprint is getting so small that before too much longer it'll simply stop being a creek and turn into nothing more than a water feature—a mere 'amenity,' as so many folks are calling it these days. [88] This is happening because every

87 I've always used the three syllable pronunciation, and until I moved to Oregon had never heard it said any other way. But Warren insists that only city folk or people from out of state pronounce it that way. "I'm just trying to get you to blend in a little better when you travel over to eastern Oregon," he would laugh. "You go around saying anything other than 'ki-oat' over there and people will snicker at your obvious urbanity." For definitive information on how to properly pronounce the word visit http://www.youtube.com/watch?v=YIPr23xyoZg
88 Beaverton Comprehensive Plan

year—hell, every month—more and more of the watershed gets covered over with concrete. And it isn't just the loss of permeability in the uplands due to new construction projects I'm talking about. Even the floodplains are getting carved up and covered over with trails and new infrastructure projects. Before long, we're going to be able to walk from Portland to Tualatin through a well-managed corridor that once used to be the nearly exclusive habitat of deer and all kinds of other critters. And sooner or later, they're going to vanish from around here. Much as I like to be able to walk the trails, I'm not totally sure we need so many, particularly in this watershed."

I was pretty wound up by then, but I could tell from their expressions that my rant wasn't putting much of a dent in their perspectives. For Al and Warren, the glass was still looking half full.

"You could be right," Warren said, as we headed for the truck. "What you're talking about is fragmentation taken to an extreme, and that would be a serious problem, for sure. But I just don't see it happening anytime soon, not now that we have a better regulatory process and a more generally aware and active group of citizens." He smiled. "People like you, in other words."

Battle Flags

The thin drizzle that had accompanied me on my walk south through Durham Park had thickened into a light but steady rain. I double-checked the water-tight seal on my camera bag and began making my way back to the truck. As I trudged along through the rain, I realized that I was retracing my first visit to the area four years earlier. Most of the small shrubs and trees I'd encountered on that first visit had flourished in the intervening years and now crowded the pathway on all sides. The plastic irrigation pipe that had helped make this particular restoration work so successful had all but vanished beneath a blanket of grasses and herbaceous plants.

At Ki-A-Kuts Bridge I paused and looked down on the mouth of Fanno Creek. Someone was fishing from the small knoll directly below the bridge. "How ya doin'?" I yelled down. The guy looked up, exposing his face to the rain. He gave me a huge grin. "Nothin' yet, but I just got here." I wished him luck and continued across the bridge to the Tualatin side.

At the south end of the bridge I entered the heavily wooded portion of the City of Tualatin's Community Park and set off down the soft-surface trail that runs along the uppermost level of the river bank. The rain was still falling, but the tree canopy above was keeping most of it at bay. I pulled off my soggy Tilley and ran the fingers of one hand through my equally soggy hair. It was late April, and the wet underbrush had leafed out enough to give the trail corridor a false sense of privacy. A runner came down the pathway towards me, a woman in her mid-thirties with rosy cheeks and a determined expression. I stepped off the narrow trail and she smiled briefly as our eyes met. Then she was gone. Seconds later a second runner, this one a man, came into view. A gray-muzzled black-lab trailed along behind, tongue lolling out and brown eyes focused on the back of his pack-leader. The man shot me a smile and brief salute as he sped by. The laboring dog barely gave me a glance.

Further down the trail I noticed a splash of bright yellow in the underbrush off to the right. A closer look revealed a stand of Oregon grape tucked away in the open spaces between the trunks of several fair-sized Douglas firs. The area was full of fading trillium and extensive patches of Pacific bleeding heart just coming into full bloom. I waded in carefully and knelt down to take a few pictures.

Oregon grape is the state's official flower. Once established, the bushes are extremely hardy and drought resistant. When they are in full bloom, as they were that day, their bright yellow blossoms contrast wonderfully with their blue-green foliage. There are two varieties of the plant, and both can be found in these woods. I was pretty sure that these were the "tall" variety (*Mahonia aquifolium*).[89] A dozen bushes had been planted in the area, and all but two of them were flourishing. The habit was upright and a little leggy, not the broader, spreading behavior seen in its close relation, *Berberis nervosa*. Each bush sported a piece of blue flagging on an upper limb, a sign that they had been planted by a restoration crew. They were set in a dense pattern, not more than a few feet apart. This kind of planting scheme was probably designed to compensate for their relatively slow rate of growth.

I pulled back some detritus at the base of one the plants and studied the ground immediately around the stem. The soil there had healed to such an extent that it was hard to tell when it might have been put into the ground. Two of the nearby plants hadn't made it. I removed the little blue banner from one of them and studied it for a moment. It had been looped over the limb the way that April Fong, science teacher and restoration-maven, had told me it should be, if it was properly affixed.[90]

"I don't tag them if I can help it," she told me once. "But they usually come to us that way from Portland's Parks and Recreation Department. They use the flags to identify particular plants during a planting, so we just leave them on. I'm a former U.S. Forest Service technician, so I definitely do *not* tie knots! I make a "U" over or under the branch (not over leaves), then pull the tails back through the middle. I make it snug but not tight. And I tie them on as far up near the top as I can, but never on the main leader."

89 Aka *Berberis aquifolium*. The other variety is *Berberis nervosa* or dull Oregon grape. Pojar & MacKinnon (1994).

90 April teaches biology and environmental science at Portland Community College's Sylvania campus. Sixteen years ago she created the Habitat Team, a student organization that focuses mostly on the restoration of the headwaters of Red Rock Creek.

The little pennant was badly faded and felt powdery to the touch. Non-professional restoration teams in this area generally use the same kind of vinyl tape for their ribbons that contractors and surveyors use to mark property lines. But many professional restoration crews won't use the stuff because it is slow to deteriorate and wildlife grazing in restored areas may accidentally ingest the pennants. Instead, they use a special "cellulosic"[91] tape that can be digested by wildlife and livestock. It breaks down completely in 6 to 24 months, faster if it's in the gut of an animal. I suspected that this particular ribbon was made from similar biodegradable materials and struck it in my pocket for later examination.

As I neared the end of the trail, I came across an area where, judging from the condition of the ribbons, a more recent restoration event had taken place. All through the understory orange, white, and yellow pennants peeked out of the shadows. Some groups of plants were also flagged with pink-and-white or orange-and-black striped tape; but before I could move off the trail and take a closer look, rain began coming down with such force that even the canopy couldn't shelter me from the impact. I made a beeline back to the truck.

While I waited for the steam on the inside of the windows to clear, I rummaged around in the glove compartment until I found the opened package of peanut butter and cheese crackers I'd tossed in there earlier in the day. I chased them down with the cold remains of the latte in my cup-holder. As I fumbled around in my rain jacket for my driving gloves, my fingers found the little scrap of blue flagging. I pulled it out and studied it for a moment.

These kinds of tiny pennants—regardless of their color, or what they are made of, or how they are affixed to a plant—are symbolic of the reasons why most Watershed Folk, like Warren and Al and all the rest, aren't prepared to pronounce Fanno Creek "Dead On Arrival" just yet. More than a million of these pennants have been distributed throughout the Tualatin Basin, each one of them tied to a piece of the living future of the watershed. There are hundreds of thousands of them in the Fanno Creek watershed alone and as many more are on the way. They are symbols of hope, to be sure; but to my way of thinking they are battle flags as well. Wherever one of these little pennants flutters in the breeze, it marks a place where someone has come into the watershed and drawn a skirmish line in the mud.

I unbuckled my seat belt and stepped out of the truck, into the rain. The flagging was pretty brittle, but I managed to loop it around the antenna anyway. I stood there for a moment, admiring my handiwork and savoring the perfume of the nearby river and its cottonwoods. Then, cold and wet, but happy, I headed for home.

91 http://www.gemplers.com/agriculture-supplies

Afterword

Why Fanno Creek?
What makes it so special?
Why should anyone care?

I used to struggle with those questions, and for the last five years a burning desire to come up with concrete answers has driven the greater part of my research. In the end, the short answer is that, for all of its interesting history and its many environmental issues, Fanno Creek is not at all unique. In fact, there are tens of thousands of creeks very much like it all over America—small, highly degraded streams that have unique histories and environmental issues of their own, but share a common set of physical and biological characteristics nonetheless.

Collectively, these characteristics are known as the Urban Stream Syndrome. The nearly universal prevalence of the Urban Stream Syndrome in our watersheds; the role this syndrome plays in the growing national water crisis; and the extreme complexity of its root-causes, all combine to make Fanno Creek's story both important and timely. That story will go forward, even though this book is finished, and you may follow it at:

http://upfannocreek.com

My sincerest hope is that something in Fanno Creek's story will motivate readers to take the few simple steps required to begin knowing their own watershed addresses. If and when that happens, here's one of the most important resources on the web:

http://water.usgs.gov/wsc/

Welcome to the watershed!

About the Author

Eric L. Lindstrom, Ed.D

Dr. Lindstrom has enjoyed success in multiple careers including professional photography, college-level teaching, and the administration of post-secondary academic programs. In 2007, shortly after retirement from academia, he began studying and photographing a small stream near his home in Portland, Oregon.

The project soon became a full-time endeavor and ultimately led to a new career as a writer/advocate focused on themes related to urban streams and their management. In addition to his work on wetlands issues he also serves on the Citizen's Action Committee for the Tualatin River Keepers; the Board of Directors for *Clearing* magazine; and as Secretary for the Natural Resources Advisory Commission/Tualatin Hills Park and Recreation District. Dr. Lindstrom is an outdoor enthusiast and enjoys sharing his passion for nature with his wife, children, and grandchildren. His public profile is available online at:

http://www.linkedin.com/pub/eric-l-lindstrom/8/413/3b5

REFERENCES / PRINTED

Abbott, C., Howe, D. & Adler, S. (1994). *Planning the Oregon way: A twenty year evaluation*. Corvallis, OR: Oregon State University Press.

Allen, J. E., Burns, M. & Burns, S.(2009). *Cataclysms on the Columbia*. Portland, OR: Ooligan Press

Alt, D. D. (2003). *Roadside geology of Oregon*. Missoula, MT: Mountain Press Publishing Company.

Ames, K. & Maschenr, H. D. G. (1999). *Peoples of the Pacific Northwest coast: Their archaeology and prehistory.* London: Thames and Hudson Ltd.

Atwater, A. (1996). *Water: A natural history*. New York: Basic Books.

Berg, L. (2007). *The first Oregonians*. Portland, OR: Oregon Council for the Humanities.

Bishop, E. M. (2004). *Hiking Oregon's geology* (2nd ed.). Seattle: The Mountaineer Books. (2003). *In search of ancient Oregon*. Portland, OR: Timber Press.

Blowers, J. (2000). *Fish stories: The historical occurrence of salmonids in the Fanno Creek watershed.* Beaverton, OR: Fans of Fanno Creek.

Boag, P. G. (1992). *Environment and experience: Settlement culture in Nineteenth Century Oregon.* *Berkely*: University of California Press.

Boyd, R. (ed.), (1999). *Indians, fire, and the land in the Pacific Northwest*. Corvallis, OR: Oregon State University Press.

Bourke, P. & DeBats, D (1995). *Washington County: Politics and community in Antebellum America.* Baltimore: John Hopkins University Press.

Campbell, J. (1991). *The power of myth*. New York: Random House.

Cressman, L. S. (1981). *The sandal and the cave: The Indians of Oregon*. Portland, OR: Beaver Books.

Corps of Engineers (1969). *Flood plain information: Tualatin River and tributaries, Washington County, Oregon.* Portland, OR: U. S. Army.

Hadidian, J., Hodge G. R. & Grandy, J. W. (1997). *Wild neighbors: The humane approach to living with wildlife*. Golden, CO: Fulcrum Press.

Houck, M. C. & Cody, M. J. (Eds) (2000). *Wild in the city: A guide to Portland's natural areas.* Corvallis: Oregon Historical Society Press.

Helfrich, G. (2004). *Humboldt's cosmos*. London: Penguin Books Ltd.

Hines, H. K. (1893). *An illustrated history of the state of Oregon*. Chicago: Lewis Publishing Company.

Juntunen, J. R., Dasch, M. D. & Rogers, A. B. (2005). *The world of the Kalapuya: A native people of western Oregon.* Philomath, OR: Benton County Historical Society.

Klein, B. (1997). *First along the river: A brief history of the U. S. environmental movement.* San Francisco: Acada Books.

Krech III, S. (1999). *The ecological Indian*. New York: W. W. Norton and Company.

Leopold, L. B. (1994). *A view of the river*. Cambridge, MA: Harvard University Press.

Louv, R. (2005). Last child in the woods. Chapel Hill, NC: Algonquin Books.

Madsen, D. B. (Ed.) (2004) *Entering America: Northeast Asia and Beringia before the last glacial maximum*. Salt Lake City: University of Utah Press.

MacWilliam, J. & Mapes, V. (1984). *Traces of the past*. Beaverton, OR: Beaverton School District

Marschner, J. (2008). *Oregon 1859: A snapshot in time*. Portland, OR: Timber Press.

McCloskey, R. (1941). *Make way for ducklings*. New York: Viking Press.

Nedeau, E. J., Smith, A. K., Stone, J. & Jepsen, S. (2009). *Freshwater mussels of the Pacific Northwest* (2nd edition). Portland, OR: Xerces Society.

O'Connor, J. E. & Costa, J.E. The world's largest floods, past and present: Their causes and magnitudes. *Circular 1254*. USGS (2012).

O'Neill, B.L., Connoly, T.J. & Freidel, D. E. (2004). A Holocene geoarchaeological record for the upper Willamette Valley, Oregon: The Long Tom and Chalker sites. *University of Oregon Anthropological Papers No. 16, Eugene, Oregon.*

Oregon Community Foundation (2006). Tualatin Valley Water Quality Endowment Fund: *Final Report, Fall 2006.*

Punke, M. L., Ozbun, T. L. & Reese, J. Early to Late Holocene Occupation at the Gee Creek Archaeological Sites in the Uplands of the Portland Basin. *Journal of Northwest Anthropology* 45(2): 159-197 2011.

Smith, K. & Ory, J. (2005). *Healthy streams plan*. Hillsboro, OR: Clean Water Services.

Spradley, J. P. (1979). *The ethnographic interview*. Belmont, CA: Wadsworth.

U.S. Army Corps of Engineers (1969). *Flood plain information: Tualatin River and tributaries*. Portland, OR: Corps of Engineers.

Walsh, C. J., Roy, A. H., Feminella, J. W., Cottingham, P. D., Grofman, P. M. (2003). The urban stream syndrome: current knowledge and a search for a cure. *The North American Benthological Society*. 24(3) 706-723.

Williams, H. (2002). *The restless Northwest*. Pullman, WA: Washington State University Press.

Wilson, B. (2000). Life on the edge. In Houck, M. C. & Cody, M.J. (Eds.), *Wild in the City* (p.5). Portland, OR: Oregon Historical Society Press.

Zenk, H. B. (1976). *Contribution to Tualatin Ethnography: Subsistence and Ethnobiology*. Unpublished MA thesis. Portland, OR: Portland State University.

REFERENCES / INTERNET

Unless otherwise specified all links were last retrieved 1/12/2012.

Audubon Society of Portland
Protect Birds in Your Backyard.
http://audubonportland.org/wcc/urban/protectingbirds

Barlow, J. (2012)
Paisley Caves yield 13,000-year old Western Stemmed points, more human DNA
http://www.eurekalert.org/pub_releases/2012-07/uoo-pcy070312.php

BgPapa (Blog).
The Story of Tellico Dam and the Snail Darter.
http://bgpappa.hubpages.com/hub/The-Story-Of-The-Snail-Darter

Bindeshwar, P. (1995).
History of the Toilet.
http://www.sulabhtoiletmuseum.org/pg02.htm

Clean Water Services.
Your Clean Water Services: Our History.
http://www.cleanwaterservices.org/AboutUs/OurStory/default.aspx

Conservation Technology Information Center, Perdue University.
Know Your Watershed.
http://www.ctic.purdue.edu/Know%20Your%20Watershed/

Cook County, Illinois, Coyote Project.
Urban Coyote Ecology and Management.
http://urbancoyoteresearch.com/

Taylor Mitchell Attack.
http://www.urbancoyoteresearch.com/Taylor_Mitchell.htm

Cowardian, L. M., Carter, V., Golet, F. C. & LaRoe, E. T. (2008)
Classification of Wetlands and Deepwater Habitats of the United States.
http://repositories.tdl.org/tamug-ir/bitstream/handle/1969.3/20139/2360-Classification%20of%20wetlands%20and%20deep-water%20habitats%20of%20the%20United%20States.pdf?sequence=1

Eckman, K., Gregersen, H. M. & Lundgren, A. L. (2000). Watershed Management and Sustainable Development: Lessons Learned and Future Directions. *USDA Forest Service Proceedings RMRS-P-13*. http://www.fs.fed.us/rm/pubs/rmrs_p013/rmrs_p013_037_043.pdf

Environmental Protection Agency
What is a 303 (d) list of impaired waters? Overview of Impaired Waters and Total Maximum Daily Loads Programs.
http://water.epa.gov/lawsregs/lawsguidance/cwa/tmdl/overview.cfm

Fritz, A. (2007).
Portland and I Lose a Passionate Friend.
http://www.amandafritz.com/node/1175;

Guest Post by Sandra Deidrich.
http://www.amandafritz.com/node/729

Fox TV
Wildlife officials look into report of coyote attacking 5-year-old.
http://www.kptv.com/story/18859237/wildlife-officials-look-into-report-of-coyote-biting-5-year-old

Gilson, L.
Oregon Archaeology.
http://www.oregon-archaeology.com/theory/pyroculture/

Hill, R. J.
The Impact of Culture and Race on Environmental Worldviews: A Study from the Southeastern U. S.
http://www.adulterc.org/Proceedings/2006/Proceedings/Hill.pdf

Hooper, P. R.
Columbia River Flood Basalt Province.
http://volcano.oregonstate.edu/vwdocs/volc_images/north_america/crb1.html

Hooper, P. R., Camp, V. E. Reidel, S. P. & Ross, M. E.
The Origin of the Columbia River Flood Basalt Province: Plume versus Nonplume Models
http://pages.uoregon.edu/rdorsey/BM/Hooper.pdf

Jenkins, D. L. (2012).
NGBPP Research at the Paisley Caves.
http://pages.uoregon.edu/ftrock/paisley_caves_description.php

Lee, K. (2008).
The Missoula Flood.
http://geology.isu.edu/Digital_Geology_Idaho/Module13/MissoulaFloodbyKeenanLee.pdf

Ohio State Research News (1/3/2005).
On the loose: Urban coyotes thrive in North American cities.
http://researchnews.osu.edu/archive/urbcoyot.htm

Oregon Department of Environmental Quality (1998).
Guidance for Conducting Beneficial Water Use Determinations at Environmental Cleanup Sites.
http://www.deq.state.or.us/lq/pubs/docs/cu/GuidanceBeneficialWaterUse.pdf

Draft Tualatin Subbasin TMDL (2005).
http://www.deq.state.or.us/wq/tmdls/docs/willamettebasin/tualatin/revision/Appendix2B3.pdf

Oregon Department of State Lands.
Essential Salmonid Habitat
http://cms.oregon.gov/DSL/PERMITS/Pages/esshabitat.aspx

Oregon Wetlands Program.
http://www.oregon.gov/DSL/WETLAND/about_us.shtml

Oregon Encyclopedia.
Tigard.
http://www.oregonencyclopedia.org/entry/view/tigard/

Oregon History Project.
Public Meeting at Champoeg, 1843.
http://www.ohs.org/education/oregonhistory/historical_records/dspDocument.cfm?doc_ID=40889788-92F9-C578-96471494DA12A34C

Oregon Historical Society.
History Minutes: Wolf Meetings.
http://www.ohs.org/education/history-minutes-wolf-meetings.cfm

Oregon State University.
Blodgett Forest Plan (Clatskanie Indians).
http://www.cof.orst.edu/cf/forests/blodgett/blodgett_plan/blodtoc.htm

Portland's Bureau of Environmental Services.
Map of Fanno Creek watershed.
http://www.portlandonline.com/bes/index.cfm?c=32199&a=315371

Fanno Force Main: Multnomah Section Rehabilitation Project.
Technical Memorandum (2008).
http://www.portlandonline.com/bes/index.cfm?a=274237&c=51206

Evolution of Portland Waste Water Treatment
http://www.portlandonline.com/bes/index.cfm?a=41962&c=31031

Punke, M. (2009).
Holocene-Aged Loess Deposits in the Uplands of the Portland Basin.
http://gsa.confex.com/gsa/2009AM/finalprogram/abstract_163522.htm

Raphels, H.
Intimate Knowledge. Center for Global, International and Regional Studies
http://repositories.cdlib.org/cgi/viewcontent.cgi?article=1021&context=cgirs

Salanger, B. (2008).
Letter to the City of Sherwood. Audubon Society of Portland.
http://audubonportland.org/backyardwildlife/brochures/coyote/coyote-letter

Sauer, C. O.
Grassland Climax, Fire, and Man.
http://www.jstor.org/pss/3894702

Seattle Times (7/3/1998).
Three Hurt in Possible Coyote Attack—Oregon Campers Gashed in Sleep.
http://community.seattletimes.nwsource.com/archive/?date=19980703&slug=2759340

Southwest Neighborhoods Inc. (SWNI).
Wild life sightings 2003—2007.
http://swni.org/bridlemile_neighborhood_association/wildlife

Terribly Write
Quotations about writing and editing.
http://terriblywrite.wordpress.com/quotations-about-writing-and-editing/

Tigard, City of.
2027 Comprehensive Plan.
http://www.tigard-or.gov/city_hall/departments/cd/docs/comp_plan_volume2.pdf

Downtown Tigard—The Heart of Our Community.
http://www.tigard-or.gov/downtown_tigard/going_green/fanno_creek_park.asp

Fanno Creek Park Master Plan (2005).
http://www.tigard-or.gov/downtown_tigard/going_green/fanno_creek_park.asp

Municipal Code, Title 18.
http://www.tigard-or.gov/business/municipal_code/title-18.asp

Tualatin Hills Park and Recreation District.
Fanno History—After Mapes, V. (1993). *The place of the beaver.* Retrieved 10/9/2008
http://www.thprd.org/facilities/fanno_history.cfm

Bauman Park—Natural Area Restoration, soft surface trail installation.
http://www.thprd.org/bondprojects/project.cfm?id=65&projectname=Bauman Park

Urban Ecosystem Research Consortium
What is UERC?
http://www.uercportland.org/?q=about_uerc

US Geological Survey.
The Boring Lava Field, Portland, Oregon. *USGS/Cascades Volcanic Observatory.*
http://vulcan.wr.usgs.gov/Volcanoes/Oregon/BoringLavaField/

Geologic Province and Thermo-Tectonic Age Maps. *USGS/Earthquake Hazards Program.*
http://earthquake.usgs.gov/research/structure/crust/maps.php

CRB Stratigraphy in the Pacific Northwest. *USGS/Oregon Water Science Center.*
http://or.water.usgs.gov/projs_dir/crbg/stratigraphy.html

Avian Cholera News. *USGS/Oregon Water Science Center.*
http://www.nwhc.usgs.gov/disease_information/avian_cholera/index.jsp

US Government.
Treaty With the Kalapuya, etc. 1885.
http://www.fws.gov/pacific/ea/tribal/treaties/kalapuya_1855.pdf

About the US Global Change Research Program (2007).
http://www.usgcrp.gov/usgcrp/nacc/education/pnw/pnw-edu-2.htm

Van Der Loo, L.
City's Sewage Saga. *The Portland Tribune.*
http://www.portlandtribune.com/news/story.php?story_id=120759941409519300

Weide, J. & Kirby, J.
Kalapuya of the Willamette Valley.
http://www.salemhist ory.net/people/native_americans.htm

Xerces Society (Lisa Schonberg)
Freshwater Mussels: Oregon floater (Anodonata oregonensis)
http://www.xerces.org/oregon-floater/

TYPEFACES

Bullen

Benton Sans

Bullen and Benton Sans are digital fonts inspired by metal typefaces issued around the turn of the twentieth century by American Type Founders Company (ATF). Bullen, designed by Juliet Shen, is an eclectic slab serif named after their publicist, Henry Lewis Bullen, who established ATF's rare book library in 1908 as a source of inspiraton and a scholarly resource for type designers in America, and to enhance appreciation of the art of printing by the general public. Benton Sans, designed by Cyrus Highsmith, is a reinterpretation and expansion of Morris Fuller Benton's News Gothic family, a sans serif typeface that was highly popular in its day and remains so in the digital era. Morris Fuller Benton was the prolific chief typeface designer of ATF, responsible for over two hundred typeface designs. Many of them are still in use today as digital fonts. Bullen and Benton Sans are issued by The Font Bureau.

MAPS

Nick Martinelli, Corvallis, OR

BOOK DESIGN

Juliet Shen, Seattle, WA

Made in the USA
San Bernardino, CA
17 March 2014